NACE
COATING INSPECTOR'S
CONDENSED LOGBOOK
Fifth Edition

Arthur K. Marshall
NACE Coating Inspector #396

NACE International
The Worldwide Corrosion Authority
15835 Park Ten Place
Houston, TX 77084

ISBN: 978-1-57590-313-2

Cover design by Michele Sandusky Jennings

NACE International
15835 Park Ten Place
Houston, TX 77084
USA
Phone: +1-281-228-6200
Fax: +1-281-228-6300
Web: nace.org

The Worldwide Corrosion Authority®

CONTENTS

THE INSPECTOR

A good inspector is conscientious. Since he or she aspires to perform quality work, the inspector researches jobs before taking them. This means learning the specifications thoroughly, including the reason for each requirement. Only if you know the reason for each specification requirement will you be able to use good judgment. You did not write the specifications. The person who did may have had good reasons for inserting provisions, which you do not think necessary or advisable. Discuss these provisions privately with your superior if you wish, but until a change is approved, see that the written specifications are followed. Be consistent in your inspection. Insist on specified results from start to finish.

NACE
COATING INSPECTOR'S
CONDENSED LOGBOOK
Fifth Edition

PROPERTY OF	
ADDRESS	
TEL	
FAX	
E-MAIL	

(NACE SEAL)

PREFACE

NACE International began providing career development courses for coating inspectors through the NACE Inspector Training and Certification Program (CIP) in 1983. Since then, as companies have realized the need for trained coating personnel, interest in the instruction and certification program has spread rapidly throughout the coating industry.

The NACE International Coating Inspector Training and Certification Program also has resulted in widespread interest in accurate and detailed record keeping. For this reason, the *NACE Coating Inspector's Logbook* was developed. The logbook is designed to be a convenient and functional tool for the coating inspector or foreman, to be used as a permanent record of an individual project, and as a complement to coating inspection daily reports.

Materials in this logbook are copyrighted by NACE. NACE allows forms to be photocopied or otherwise reproduced in reasonable quantities as necessary, provided that the copies relate to the project for which the book was purchased. Additional logbooks can be ordered through the NACE *First-*Service, Tel: +1 281-228-6223 or E-mail: FirstService@nace.org.

Arthur K. Marshall
NACE Coating Inspector #396

INTRODUCTION

The *NACE Coating Inspector's Logbook* is intended to be used as part of the historical record of an individual coatings project. Used with coating inspection daily report sheets or other proprietary daily report forms, the logbook will provide a clear record of a project, years after the work has been completed and memories have faded.

The *NACE Coating Inspector's Logbook* is divided into six primary sections:

1. **General Project Data**—including site safety information, client and site information forms, and a quality-control checklist

2. **Project Records and Reports**—including forms for pre-inspection reporting, forms for production records, materials and equipment records, and abrasive sieve test reporting

3. **Inspector's Daily Log**—providing space for daily comments by the inspector

4. **Warranty Inspection**

5. **Reference Data**—including a variety of reference materials for quick technical support

6. **Work Verification Data**—summary of protective coatings related work experience.

Users of the *NACE Coating Inspector's Logbook* are encouraged to provide complete and detailed information, where applicable to the project, and to remember that the information included in this logbook could prove vital in verifying the quality of the coating project, justifying payments, investigating reported problems, or initiating or defending penalty clause claims. Suggestions for additional information to be included in future editions of the *NACE Coating Inspector's Logbook* are always welcomed by NACE.

SECTION I
GENERAL PROJECT DATA

SITE SAFETY INFORMATION

Job Title

Specific Location

Emergency Telephone Numbers
Police:
Fire:
Medic:
Safety Department:
Security:

Material Safety Data Sheet Information Number(s)

Other

CLIENT & SITE INFORMATION

Client Name:	
E-mail:	
Purchase Order #	Date:
Job Title:	
Address/Location:	
Telephone:	Fax:
Specific Location:	
Contract Engineer:	
Telephone:	E-mail:
Site Engineer:	
Telephone:	E-mail:
Security Telephone:	
Other:	

MISCELLANEOUS ADDRESSES

Client Name:	Title:
Company:	
Address:	
Phone:	E-mail:
Job Title:	

Client Name:	Title:
Company:	
Address:	
Phone:	E-mail:
Job Title:	

Client Name:	Title:
Company:	
Address:	
Phone:	E-mail:
Job Title:	

Client Name:	Title:
Company:	
Address:	
Phone:	E-mail:
Job Title:	

Client Name:	Title:
Company:	
Address:	
Phone:	E-mail:
Job Title:	

Client Name:	Title:
Company:	
Address:	
Phone:	E-mail:
Job Title:	

MISCELLANEOUS ADDRESSES

Client Name:	Title:
Company:	
Address:	
Phone:	E-mail:
Job Title:	

Client Name:	Title:
Company:	
Address:	
Phone:	E-mail:
Job Title:	

Client Name:	Title:
Company:	
Address:	
Phone:	E-mail:
Job Title:	

Client Name:	Title:
Company:	
Address:	
Phone:	E-mail:
Job Title:	

Client Name:	Title:
Company:	
Address:	
Phone:	E-mail:
Job Title:	

Client Name:	Title:
Company:	
Address:	
Phone:	E-mail:
Job Title:	

MISCELLANEOUS INFORMATION

CERTIFICATIONS & INSPECTION EQUIPMENT NUMBERS

Contractor Name:_____ Job Title:_____

Specific Location:_____ Date: _____

SSPC-QP-1 #: _____ QP-2#: _____ QP-3 #: _____

CONTRACTOR EMPLOYEE'S NACE CERTIFICATION NUMBERS & LEVELS

Contractor Name:_____

NACE Certification #: _____ Level: _____ Exp. Date: _____

NACE Certification #: _____ Level: _____ Exp. Date: _____

Other Certification Numbers Applicable to Contractor:_____

(Example SSPC Coating Specialist) Exp. Date: _____

Contractor Inspection Equipment

Description	Serial Number	Calibration Date	Calibration Method
_____	_____	_____	_____
_____	_____	_____	_____
_____	_____	_____	_____
_____	_____	_____	_____
_____	_____	_____	_____
_____	_____	_____	_____

Inspector Name: _____

NACE Certification #: _____ Level: _____ Exp. Date: _____

Other Certification Numbers Applicable to Inspector: _____

(Example SSPC Coating Specialist) Exp. Date: _____

Inspector's Inspection Equipment

Description	Serial Number	Calibration Date	Calibration Method
_____	_____	_____	_____
_____	_____	_____	_____
_____	_____	_____	_____
_____	_____	_____	_____
_____	_____	_____	_____
_____	_____	_____	_____

Report # _____

CERTIFICATIONS & INSPECTION EQUIPMENT NUMBERS

Contractor Name: _____ Job Title: _____

Specific Location: _____ Date: _____

SSPC-QP-1 #: _____ QP-2#: _____ QP-3 #: _____

CONTRACTOR EMPLOYEE'S NACE CERTIFICATION NUMBERS & LEVELS

Contractor Name: _____

NACE Certification #: _____ Level: _____ Exp. Date: _____

NACE Certification #: _____ Level: _____ Exp. Date: _____

Other Certification Numbers Applicable to Contractor: _____

(Example SSPC Coating Specialist) Exp. Date: _____

Contractor Inspection Equipment

Description	Serial Number	Calibration Date	Calibration Method
_____	_____	_____	_____
_____	_____	_____	_____
_____	_____	_____	_____
_____	_____	_____	_____
_____	_____	_____	_____
_____	_____	_____	_____

Inspector Name: _____

NACE Certification #: _____ Level: _____ Exp. Date: _____

Other Certification Numbers Applicable to Inspector: _____

(Example SSPC Coating Specialist) Exp. Date: _____

Inspector's Inspection Equipment

Description	Serial Number	Calibration Date	Calibration Method
_____	_____	_____	_____
_____	_____	_____	_____
_____	_____	_____	_____
_____	_____	_____	_____
_____	_____	_____	_____
_____	_____	_____	_____

Report # _____

COATING INSPECTOR'S CHECKLIST[1]

SPECIFICATION
Have it ☐
Read it ☐
Understand it ☐

PRE-JOB CONFERENCE
Request one ☐
Attend it ☐
Participate actively ☐
Know & understand safety rules ☐

COATING SCHEDULE
Know where coating will take place ☐

PRE-INSPECTION
Locate areas that will be hard to coat ☐
Weld spatter ☐
Weld flux ☐
Skip welds ☐
Rough welds ☐
Sharp corners ☐
Laminations ☐

SURFACE PREPARATION
Observe safety rules ☐
Correct abrasives ☐
Abrasive clean ☐
Compressed air clean ☐
Nozzle pressure adequate ☐
Anchor pattern as specified ☐
All dust & contaminants removed ☐
Neutral surface ☐
Check pH level ☐
Check for soluble salts ☐
Check for lead/heavy metals ☐
Surface as called for in specification ☐
Surface defects corrected ☐
Weather suitable for abrasive blasting ☐
Items not to be coated protected ☐

COATINGS
Observe safety rules ☐
Coatings are those specified ☐
Checked shelf life ☐
Stored correctly ☐
Checked coating temperature ☐
Coatings correctly mixed and agitated ☐
Coatings correctly thinned ☐
Induction time checked ☐
Solid content checked after thinning ☐
Coatings have not exceeded pot life ☐

COATING APPLICATION ☐
Observe safety rules ☐
Weather OK ☐
Ambient conditions OK ☐
Clean surface ☐
Application equipment clean & operable ☐
Enter application method on daily log ☐
Correct WFT ☐
Correct DFT ☐
No flaws ☐
Runs ☐
Dry spray ☐
Holidays ☐
Other ☐
Stripe/brush welds, bolts,
　sharp edges and similar areas ☐
Inspect color, gloss, & finish ☐

REPORTS
Take all measurements required ☐
Check cure & adhesion; log method used ☐
Record and report as required ☐
Record general information on
　Inspection Daily Log ☐

[1] From the NACE Coating Inspector Training
　and Certification Program.

See: Checklists for Coating Concrete and Surface Preparation with Water, pp. 213 & 217

SECTION II
PROJECT RECORDS & REPORTS

As a rule, all entries should be initialed. This practice simplifies investigations of coating problems and transition from one person to the next. Further, a CIP seal, if applicable, should be placed on each section fly sheet verifying the credentials of the person logging the entries and/or the level three inspector responsible for review. All entries should be made with pen rather than pencil, which could be erased. Corrections should be crossed out and initialed, not erased.

Each job documented in this book is separated by the job title, specific location, and date the job occurred. It may be helpful to place a rubber band over the page of your last entry for quick reference. Use as many pages as needed to document each phase.

Note: Visit NACE Online at nace.org or call NACE FirstService at +1 281-228-6223 to reorder a copy of this book.

RATING OF PAINTED SURFACE
ASTM-D610/SSPC-Vis 2

SCALE AND DESCRIPTION OF RUST GRADES

Rust Grades*	Description	ASTM-SSPC Photographic Standard
10	no rusting or less than 0.01 percent of surface rusted	unnecessary
9	minute rusting less than 0.03 percent of surface rusted	No. 9
8*	few isolated rust spots. less than 0.1 percent of surface rusted	No. 8
7	less than 0.3 percent of surface rusted	none
6*	extensive rust spots but less than 1 percent of surface rusted	No. 6
5	rusting to the extent of 3 percent of surface rusted	none
4*	rusting to the extent of 10 percent of surface rusted	No. 4
3*	approximately one sixth of the surface rusted	none
2	approximately one third of the surface rusted	none
1	approximately one half of the surface rusted	none
0*	approximately 100 percent of the surface rusted	unnecessary

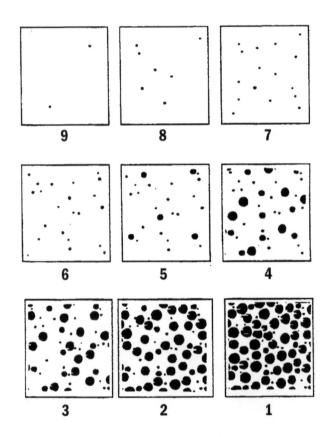

PRE-INSPECTION COMMENTS

JOB TITLE	INSPECTOR
	INSPECTION DATE
SPECIFIC LOCATION	
	ENVIRONMENT

COMMENTS	SQ. FT. TO PAINT	
	REPAINT DATE	
	SQ. FT. TO TOUCH UP	
	TOUCH UP DATE	

PAINT HISTORY

RIGGING COMMENTS

COMPLETE INFORMATION BELOW

% Insufficient Top Coat	ASTM Rust Grade Ref. 1–9 (see p. 16 or 309)	Condition of Unpainted Steel Ref. A B C D	Specific Location

A. Steel surface covered completely with adherent mill scale with little, if any, rust.
B. Steel surface which has begun to rust, and from which the mill scale has begun to flake.
C. Steel surface from which the mill scale has rusted away or from which it can be scraped, but with little pitting visible to the naked eye.
D. Steel surface on which the mill scale has rusted away and where pitting is visible to the naked eye.

Report #	

PRE-INSPECTION COMMENTS

JOB TITLE		INSPECTOR	
		INSPECTION DATE	
SPECIFIC LOCATION			
		ENVIRONMENT	
COMMENTS		SQ. FT. TO PAINT	
		REPAINT DATE	
		SQ. FT. TO TOUCH UP	
		TOUCH UP DATE	

PAINT HISTORY

RIGGING COMMENTS

COMPLETE INFORMATION BELOW

% Insufficient Top Coat	ASTM Rust Grade Ref. 1–9 (see p. 16 or 309)	Condition of Unpainted Steel Ref. A B C D	Specific Location

A. Steel surface covered completely with adherent mill scale with little, if any, rust.
B. Steel surface which has begun to rust, and from which the mill scale has begun to flake.
C. Steel surface from which the mill scale has rusted away or from which it can be scraped, but with little pitting visible to the naked eye.
D. Steel surface on which the mill scale has rusted away and where pitting is visible to the naked eye.

Report #

PRE-INSPECTION FOR LEAD OR HEAVY METALS

PRE-INSPECTION FOR LEAD OR HEAVY METALS

OWNER:		INSPECTOR:		DATE:		LEAD OR HEAVY METALS IDENTIFIED CHECK APPROPRIATE BOX BELOW		
HEAVY METAL TYPE:				JOB TITLE:		YES	% BY WEIGHT	NO
GENERAL DESCRIPTION OF STRUCTURE OR EQUIPMENT (INCLUDE LOCATION):				SPECIFIC STRUCTURE/EQUIPMENT IDENTIFICATION:				
LAB:				TEST METHOD:				
OFFICIAL NOTIFIED:								
COMMENTS:								
REPORT #:								

PRE-INSPECTION FOR LEAD OR HEAVY METALS

OWNER:		INSPECTOR:		DATE:		LEAD OR HEAVY METALS IDENTIFIED CHECK APPROPRIATE BOX BELOW		
						YES	% BY WEIGHT	NO
HEAVY METAL TYPE:		JOB TITLE:						
GENERAL DESCRIPTION OF STRUCTURE OR EQUIPMENT (INCLUDE LOCATION):		SPECIFIC STRUCTURE/EQUIPMENT IDENTIFICATION:						
LAB:		TEST METHOD:						
OFFICIAL NOTIFIED:								
COMMENTS:								
REPORT #:								

21

PRE-INSPECTION FOR LEAD OR HEAVY METALS

OWNER:

INSPECTOR:

DATE:

HEAVY METAL TYPE:

JOB TITLE:

GENERAL DESCRIPTION OF STRUCTURE OR EQUIPMENT (INCLUDE LOCATION):

SPECIFIC STRUCTURE/EQUIPMENT IDENTIFICATION:	LEAD OR HEAVY METALS IDENTIFIED CHECK APPROPRIATE BOX BELOW		
	YES	% BY WEIGHT	NO

LAB:

TEST METHOD:

OFFICIAL NOTIFIED:

COMMENTS:

REPORT #:

PRE-INSPECTION FOR LEAD OR HEAVY METALS

OWNER:		
INSPECTOR:		
HEAVY METAL TYPE:		
JOB TITLE:		
DATE:		

GENERAL DESCRIPTION OF STRUCTURE OR EQUIPMENT (INCLUDE LOCATION):	SPECIFIC STRUCTURE/EQUIPMENT IDENTIFICATION:	LEAD OR HEAVY METALS IDENTIFIED CHECK APPROPRIATE BOX BELOW		
		YES	% BY WEIGHT	NO

LAB:

TEST METHOD:

OFFICIAL NOTIFIED:

COMMENTS:

REPORT #:

PRE-INSPECTION FOR LEAD OR HEAVY METALS

OWNER:

INSPECTOR:

DATE:

HEAVY METAL TYPE:

JOB TITLE:

GENERAL DESCRIPTION OF STRUCTURE OR EQUIPMENT (INCLUDE LOCATION):

SPECIFIC STRUCTURE/EQUIPMENT IDENTIFICATION:

	LEAD OR HEAVY METALS IDENTIFIED CHECK APPROPRIATE BOX BELOW		
	YES	% BY WEIGHT	NO

LAB:

TEST METHOD:

OFFICIAL NOTIFIED:

COMMENTS:

REPORT #:

PRE-INSPECTION FOR SOLUBLE SALTS OR OTHER CONTAMINANTS

PRE-INSPECTION FOR SOLUBLE SALTS OR OTHER CONTAMINANTS

OWNER:		INSPECTOR:		DATE:			SOLUBLE SALT OR OTHER CONTAMINANT IDENTIFICATION CHECK APPROPRIATE BOX		
CONTAMINANT TYPE:			JOB TITLE:				YES	µg/cm² or PPM	NO
GENERAL DESCRIPTION OF STRUCTURE OR EQUIPMENT (INCLUDE LOCATION):			SPECIFIC STRUCTURE/EQUIPMENT IDENTIFICATION:						
LAB:		TEST METHOD:							
OFFICIAL NOTIFIED:									
COMMENTS:									
REPORT #:									

PRE-INSPECTION FOR SOLUBLE SALTS OR OTHER CONTAMINANTS

OWNER:

INSPECTOR:

DATE:

CONTAMINANT TYPE:

JOB TITLE:

GENERAL DESCRIPTION OF STRUCTURE OR EQUIPMENT (INCLUDE LOCATION):

SPECIFIC STRUCTURE/EQUIPMENT IDENTIFICATION:

	SOLUBLE SALT OR OTHER CONTAMINANT IDENTIFICATION CHECK APPROPRIATE BOX		
	YES	$\mu g/cm^2$ or PPM	NO

LAB:

TEST METHOD:

OFFICIAL NOTIFIED:

COMMENTS:

REPORT #:

PRE-INSPECTION FOR SOLUBLE SALTS OR OTHER CONTAMINANTS

OWNER:	INSPECTOR:	DATE:

CONTAMINANT TYPE:	JOB TITLE:

| | | SOLUBLE SALT OR OTHER CONTAMINANT IDENTIFICATION CHECK APPROPRIATE BOX | | |
GENERAL DESCRIPTION OF STRUCTURE OR EQUIPMENT (INCLUDE LOCATION):	SPECIFIC STRUCTURE/EQUIPMENT IDENTIFICATION:	YES	μg/cm² or PPM	NO

LAB:	TEST METHOD:

OFFICIAL NOTIFIED:

COMMENTS:

REPORT #:

VOC EMISSION LOG

The following form provides typical documentation for effectively making calculations to meet applicable regulation permits, record keeping requirements, and emission limitations. The owner/end user may provide their own forms, but if not, the following example may be copied and used as a guide to document the appropriate information.

VOC EMISSION LOG
Example

Remit to: _____
Department: _____

DATE	START TIME	STOP TIME	SAP WO #	APPLICATION	MANUFACTURER OF SPRAYING EQUIPMENT (3)	MODEL TYPE or NO. (3)	TIP SIZE (INCHES) (3)	EQUIPMENT PAINTED or COATED (4)	JOB LOCATION	PRODUCT MANUFACTURER	PRODUCT NAME	PRODUCT BATCH NO.	QUANTITY USED	UNIT OF MEASURE	DENSITY (lbs./gal)	% VOC CONTENT (6)	LB per EVENT VOC EMISSIONS
12/1/2014	6:30	5:00	4166948	con spray	devil bliss	MBA	D	piping	wwu	carboline	thinner 33		15	gal	7.42	100	111.300
																	TPM

COMPANY: _____ PHONE: _____

CLIENT: _____ FAX: _____

STRUCTURE IDENTIFICATION & LOCATION: _____

DATE	START TIME	STOP TIME	SAP WO #	APPLICATION	MANUFACTURER OF SPRAYING EQUIPMENT (3)	MODEL TYPE or NO. (3)	TIP SIZE (INCHES) (3)	EQUIPMENT PAINTED or COATED (4)	JOB LOCATION	PRODUCT MANUFACTURER	PRODUCT NAME	PRODUCT BATCH NO.	QUANTITY USED	UNIT OF MEASURE	DENSITY (lbs./gal)	% VOC CONTENT (6)	LB per EVENT VOC EMISSIONS
12/1/2014	6:30	5:00	4185145	abrasive blast	Schmitt	8 ton	#7	piping	blastyard	barton	Alkylal Garnet 30/60		3	bulk bags			
																	TPM

COMPANY: _____ PHONE: _____

CLIENT: _____ FAX: _____

STRUCTURE IDENTIFICATION & LOCATION: _____

[1] Logsheet must be completed for each painting/coating activity & given to the designated department at least monthly to meet applicable regulatory/permit record keeping requirements and emmissions limitations.
[2] State if the paint/coating was applied via the following methods: brushing, rolling, dipping, spraying, etc.
[3] Enter "N/A" if the paint/coating was applied using a method other than spraying.
[4] State the type of equipment painted or coated (i.e. tank, pipe, etc.)
[5] Document the equipment name and/or the location of the paint/coating activity.
[6] Density and VOC values can be found on product data sheets or MSDS sheets located at V:\safety and environmental\Groups\Environom\AIR\MSS Emission Calculations\2011\MSDS Sheets

RECORD OF MATERIALS STORED AND USED AT SITE

This section is primarily used for time and material jobs. It can also be used to justify monthly payments and to refer back to for estimating the cost of future jobs.

RECORD OF MATERIALS STORED AND USED AT SITE

JOB TITLE	
SPECIFIC LOCATION	
MATERIAL TYPE & NO.	
MANUFACTURER:	

DATE	QUANTITY DELIVERED	QUANTITY USED	BALANCE OF MATERIALS ON SITE

ADDITIONAL COMMENTS

REPORT #	

RECORD OF MATERIALS STORED AND USED AT SITE

JOB TITLE	
SPECIFIC LOCATION	
MATERIAL TYPE & NO.	
MANUFACTURER:	

DATE	QUANTITY DELIVERED	QUANTITY USED	BALANCE OF MATERIALS ON SITE

ADDITIONAL COMMENTS

REPORT #	

RECORD OF MATERIALS STORED AND USED AT SITE

JOB TITLE	
SPECIFIC LOCATION	
MATERIAL TYPE & NO.	
MANUFACTURER:	

DATE	QUANTITY DELIVERED	QUANTITY USED	BALANCE OF MATERIALS ON SITE

ADDITIONAL COMMENTS

REPORT #	

34

RECORD OF MATERIALS STORED AND USED AT SITE

JOB TITLE	
SPECIFIC LOCATION	
MATERIAL TYPE & NO.	
MANUFACTURER:	

DATE	QUANTITY DELIVERED	QUANTITY USED	BALANCE OF MATERIALS ON SITE

ADDITIONAL COMMENTS

| REPORT # | |

RECORD OF MATERIALS STORED AND USED AT SITE

JOB TITLE	
SPECIFIC LOCATION	
MATERIAL TYPE & NO.	
MANUFACTURER:	

DATE	QUANTITY DELIVERED	QUANTITY USED	BALANCE OF MATERIALS ON SITE

ADDITIONAL COMMENTS

| REPORT # | |

EQUIPMENT RECORD

EQUIPMENT RECORD

JOB TITLE	
SPECIFIC LOCATION	

QUANTITY	EQUIPMENT DESCRIPTION	START DATE	FINISH DATE

ADDITIONAL COMMENTS

REPORT #	

EQUIPMENT RECORD

JOB TITLE				
SPECIFIC LOCATION				
QUANTITY	EQUIPMENT DESCRIPTION		START DATE	FINISH DATE

ADDITIONAL COMMENTS

REPORT #	

39

EQUIPMENT RECORD

JOB TITLE			
SPECIFIC LOCATION			
QUANTITY	EQUIPMENT DESCRIPTION	START DATE	FINISH DATE

ADDITIONAL COMMENTS

REPORT #	

MAN-HOUR ALLOCATION

To complement the recording of materials and equipment on the jobsite, it is important to separate productive man-hours from payroll hours. This action creates a clear picture of critical path vs. less productive and downtime. With this information, the owner, inspector, and contractor can better predict future costs and quotes. Improvements may be incorporated or specified for better time management, which enhances competitiveness and overall quality.

MAN-HOUR ALLOCATIONS

Job Title: _____

Inspector: _____

Location: _____

Productive Man-Hour Allocations									Total Man-hours Allocated		
Week of: _____	Mon	Tue	Wed	Thur	Fri	Sat	Sun	Week	Prior	Grand
Sandblasting										
Coal slag blasting										
Copper slag blasting										
Garnet blasting										
Third party surface prep										
Priming										
Stripe coat										
Intermediate coat										
Top coat										
Special coat										
Mobe/Demobe										
Safety meeting										
Rigging										
Preparation										
Protection										
Pressure wash										
Containment										
Clean-up										
Productive totals										
Non-Productive Man-hour Allocations									Total Man-hours Allocated		
Week of: _____	Mon	Tue	Wed	Thur	Fri	Sat	Sun	Week	Prior	Grand
Weather										
Permit problems										
Safety stand-down										
Special meetings										
Operational delay										
Down-time										
Meals/breaks										
Other										
Non-productive totals										
Grand totals										
Est. man-hours allotted:			Current man-hour total:				Total man-hours remaining:			

MAN-HOUR ALLOCATIONS

Job Title: _____

Inspector: _____

Location: _____

Productive Man-Hour Allocations									Total Man-hours Allocated		
Week of: _____	Mon	Tue	Wed	Thur	Fri	Sat	Sun	Week	Prior	Grand
Sandblasting										
Coal slag blasting										
Copper slag blasting										
Garnet blasting										
Third party surface prep										
Priming										
Stripe coat										
Intermediate coat										
Top coat										
Special coat										
Mobe/Demobe										
Safety meeting										
Rigging										
Preparation										
Protection										
Pressure wash										
Containment										
Clean-up										
Productive totals										
Non-Productive Man-hour Allocations									Total Man-hours Allocated		
Week of: _____	Mon	Tue	Wed	Thur	Fri	Sat	Sun	Week	Prior	Grand
Weather										
Permit problems										
Safety stand-down										
Special meetings										
Operational delay										
Down-time										
Meals/breaks										
Other										
Non-productive totals										
Grand totals										
Est. man-hours allotted:			**Current man-hour total:**				**Total man-hours remaining:**			

MAN-HOUR ALLOCATIONS

Job Title: _____

Inspector: _____

Location: _____

Productive Man-Hour Allocations									Total Man-hours Allocated		
Week of: _____	Mon	Tue	Wed	Thur	Fri	Sat	Sun	Week	Prior	Grand
Sandblasting										
Coal slag blasting										
Copper slag blasting										
Garnet blasting										
Third party surface prep										
Priming										
Stripe coat										
Intermediate coat										
Top coat										
Special coat										
Mobe/Demobe										
Safety meeting										
Rigging										
Preparation										
Protection										
Pressure wash										
Containment										
Clean-up										
Productive totals										
Non-Productive Man-hour Allocations									Total Man-hours Allocated		
Week of: _____	Mon	Tue	Wed	Thur	Fri	Sat	Sun	Week	Prior	Grand
Weather										
Permit problems										
Safety stand-down										
Special meetings										
Operational delay										
Down-time										
Meals/breaks										
Other										
Non-productive totals										
Grand totals										
Est. man-hours allotted:			**Current man-hour total:**				**Total man-hours remaining:**			

MAN-HOUR ALLOCATIONS

Job Title: _____

Inspector: _____

Location: _____

Productive Man-Hour Allocations									Total Man-hours Allocated		
Week of: _____	Mon	Tue	Wed	Thur	Fri	Sat	Sun	Week	Prior	Grand
Sandblasting											
Coal slag blasting											
Copper slag blasting											
Garnet blasting											
Third party surface prep											
Priming											
Stripe coat											
Intermediate coat											
Top coat											
Special coat											
Mobe/Demobe											
Safety meeting											
Rigging											
Preparation											
Protection											
Pressure wash											
Containment											
Clean-up											
Productive totals											
Non-Productive Man-hour Allocations									Total Man-hours Allocated		
Week of: _____	Mon	Tue	Wed	Thur	Fri	Sat	Sun	Week	Prior	Grand
Weather											
Permit problems											
Safety stand-down											
Special meetings											
Operational delay											
Down-time											
Meals/breaks											
Other											
Non-productive totals											
Grand totals											
Est. man-hours allotted:			Current man-hour total:				Total man-hours remaining:			

MAN-HOUR ALLOCATIONS

Job Title: _____

Inspector: _____

Location: _____

Productive Man-Hour Allocations								Total Man-hours Allocated		
Week of: _____	Mon	Tue	Wed	Thur	Fri	Sat	Sun	Week	Prior	Grand
Sandblasting										
Coal slag blasting										
Copper slag blasting										
Garnet blasting										
Third party surface prep										
Priming										
Stripe coat										
Intermediate coat										
Top coat										
Special coat										
Mobe/Demobe										
Safety meeting										
Rigging										
Preparation										
Protection										
Pressure wash										
Containment										
Clean-up										
Productive totals										
Non-Productive Man-hour Allocations								Total Man-hours Allocated		
Week of: _____	Mon	Tue	Wed	Thur	Fri	Sat	Sun	Week	Prior	Grand
Weather										
Permit problems										
Safety stand-down										
Special meetings										
Operational delay										
Down-time										
Meals/breaks										
Other										
Non-productive totals										
Grand totals										
Est. man-hours allotted:			Current man-hour total:				Total man-hours remaining:			

MAN-HOUR ALLOCATIONS

Job Title: _____

Inspector: _____

Location: _____

Productive Man-Hour Allocations								Total Man-hours Allocated		
Week of: _____	Mon	Tue	Wed	Thur	Fri	Sat	Sun	Week	Prior	Grand
Sandblasting										
Coal slag blasting										
Copper slag blasting										
Garnet blasting										
Third party surface prep										
Priming										
Stripe coat										
Intermediate coat										
Top coat										
Special coat										
Mobe/Demobe										
Safety meeting										
Rigging										
Preparation										
Protection										
Pressure wash										
Containment										
Clean-up										
Productive totals										
Non-Productive Man-hour Allocations								Total Man-hours Allocated		
Week of: _____	Mon	Tue	Wed	Thur	Fri	Sat	Sun	Week	Prior	Grand
Weather										
Permit problems										
Safety stand-down										
Special meetings										
Operational delay										
Down-time										
Meals/breaks										
Other										
Non-productive totals										
Grand totals										
Est. man-hours allotted:			Current man-hour total:				Total man-hours remaining:			

MAN-HOUR ALLOCATIONS

Job Title: _____

Inspector: _____

Location: _____

Productive Man-Hour Allocations									Total Man-hours Allocated		
Week of: _____	Mon	Tue	Wed	Thur	Fri	Sat	Sun	Week	Prior	Grand
Sandblasting											
Coal slag blasting											
Copper slag blasting											
Garnet blasting											
Third party surface prep											
Priming											
Stripe coat											
Intermediate coat											
Top coat											
Special coat											
Mobe/Demobe											
Safety meeting											
Rigging											
Preparation											
Protection											
Pressure wash											
Containment											
Clean-up											
Productive totals											
Non-Productive Man-hour Allocations									Total Man-hours Allocated		
Week of: _____	Mon	Tue	Wed	Thur	Fri	Sat	Sun	Week	Prior	Grand
Weather											
Permit problems											
Safety stand-down											
Special meetings											
Operational delay											
Down-time											
Meals/breaks											
Other											
Non-productive totals											
Grand totals											
Est. man-hours allotted:			**Current man-hour total:**				**Total man-hours remaining:**			

MAN-HOUR ALLOCATIONS

Job Title: _____

Inspector: _____

Location: _____

Productive Man-Hour Allocations								Total Man-hours Allocated		
Week of: _____	Mon	Tue	Wed	Thur	Fri	Sat	Sun	Week	Prior	Grand
Sandblasting										
Coal slag blasting										
Copper slag blasting										
Garnet blasting										
Third party surface prep										
Priming										
Stripe coat										
Intermediate coat										
Top coat										
Special coat										
Mobe/Demobe										
Safety meeting										
Rigging										
Preparation										
Protection										
Pressure wash										
Containment										
Clean-up										
Productive totals										
Non-Productive Man-hour Allocations								Total Man-hours Allocated		
Week of: _____	Mon	Tue	Wed	Thur	Fri	Sat	Sun	Week	Prior	Grand
Weather										
Permit problems										
Safety stand-down										
Special meetings										
Operational delay										
Down-time										
Meals/breaks										
Other										
Non-productive totals										
Grand totals										
Est. man-hours allotted:			Current man-hour total:				Total man-hours remaining:			

MAN-HOUR ALLOCATIONS

Job Title: _____

Inspector: _____

Location: _____

Productive Man-Hour Allocations									Total Man-hours Allocated		
Week of: _____	Mon	Tue	Wed	Thur	Fri	Sat	Sun	Week	Prior	Grand
Sandblasting											
Coal slag blasting											
Copper slag blasting											
Garnet blasting											
Third party surface prep											
Priming											
Stripe coat											
Intermediate coat											
Top coat											
Special coat											
Mobe/Demobe											
Safety meeting											
Rigging											
Preparation											
Protection											
Pressure wash											
Containment											
Clean-up											
Productive totals											
Non-Productive Man-hour Allocations									**Total Man-hours Allocated**		
Week of: _____	Mon	Tue	Wed	Thur	Fri	Sat	Sun	Week	Prior	Grand
Weather											
Permit problems											
Safety stand-down											
Special meetings											
Operational delay											
Down-time											
Meals/breaks											
Other											
Non-productive totals											
Grand totals											
Est. man-hours allotted:			Current man-hour total:				Total man-hours remaining:			

MAN-HOUR ALLOCATIONS

Job Title: _____

Inspector: _____

Location: _____

Productive Man-Hour Allocations									Total Man-hours Allocated		
Week of: _____	Mon	Tue	Wed	Thur	Fri	Sat	Sun	Week	Prior	Grand
Sandblasting										
Coal slag blasting										
Copper slag blasting										
Garnet blasting										
Third party surface prep										
Priming										
Stripe coat										
Intermediate coat										
Top coat										
Special coat										
Mobe/Demobe										
Safety meeting										
Rigging										
Preparation										
Protection										
Pressure wash										
Containment										
Clean-up										
Productive totals										
Non-Productive Man-hour Allocations									Total Man-hours Allocated		
Week of: _____	Mon	Tue	Wed	Thur	Fri	Sat	Sun	Week	Prior	Grand
Weather										
Permit problems										
Safety stand-down										
Special meetings										
Operational delay										
Down-time										
Meals/breaks										
Other										
Non-productive totals										
Grand totals										
Est. man-hours allotted:			Current man-hour total:				Total man-hours remaining:			

MAN-HOUR ALLOCATIONS

Job Title: _____

Inspector: _____

Location: _____

Productive Man-Hour Allocations								Total Man-hours Allocated		
Week of: _____	Mon	Tue	Wed	Thur	Fri	Sat	Sun	Week	Prior	Grand
Sandblasting										
Coal slag blasting										
Copper slag blasting										
Garnet blasting										
Third party surface prep										
Priming										
Stripe coat										
Intermediate coat										
Top coat										
Special coat										
Mobe/Demobe										
Safety meeting										
Rigging										
Preparation										
Protection										
Pressure wash										
Containment										
Clean-up										
Productive totals										
Non-Productive Man-hour Allocations								Total Man-hours Allocated		
Week of: _____	Mon	Tue	Wed	Thur	Fri	Sat	Sun	Week	Prior	Grand
Weather										
Permit problems										
Safety stand-down										
Special meetings										
Operational delay										
Down-time										
Meals/breaks										
Other										
Non-productive totals										
Grand totals										
Est. man-hours allotted:			**Current man-hour total:**				**Total man-hours remaining:**			

JOB HAZARD
ANALYSIS FORM

The items contained on these forms are minimum standards only. When overseeing any type of construction, be familiar with OSHA and other applicable standards.

SAFETY FIRST!

JOB HAZARD ANALYSIS FORM

Date:	Inspection by:
Jobsite:	Job Number:
Owner:	Specific Location
Client:	
Contact:	Telephone:
Owner/Client Safety Officer:	
Local Medical Facility:	

Physical Hazards:	Check those that apply, listing specific risks and actions to be taken	Special Training Req.	OSHA Ref. Section
Fall/Trip			1926.104
Scaffolding	Type?	X	1926.451
Confined Spaces		X	1926.146
Fire	Extinguishers Inspected?		1926.150
Explosion			
Water (Drowning)			1926.106
Electrical			1926.302
Noise	Expected level dBA?		1926.52
Hazardous Energy		X	1910.147
Heat Stress			

Chemical Hazards	List Manufacturer and Name or Number	MSDS Reviewed?
Paints: Primers		
Paints: Finishes		
Polyurethane (isocyanates)		
Solvents		
Abrasives		
Dust/Fumes/Mists		
Fuels		
Acid Corrosives		

List of Hazardous Materials and MSDS given to the Customer? (Y/N)	Date		1926.59

JOB HAZARD ANALYSIS FORM (continued)

Date:			Inspection by:	

Environmental Hazards				OSHA Ref. Section
Lead-Based Paint				1926.62
Requires: compliance plan, training, medical monitoring, hygiene facilities, exposure monitoring, warning signs.				
Surface Contaminants				
Process Chemicals				
Plant Emissions				
Other Contractors' Materials				
Client Hazardous Materials	(PSM)	Emergency plan reviewed?		1910.119

Evaluate Hazards per OSHA 1910.132 (PPE) and Identify Personal Protective Equipment Required

Head Protection (ANSI Z89.1-1986)	Respiratory Protection (1926.103)	Fall Protection (1926.103)	ANSI Sec.
Hard Hats	1/2 Mask Respirators	Safety Harness	A10.14-1991
Eye Protection (ANSI Z87.1-1989)	Cartridge:	Lanyard with Shock Absorber	Z359.1-1992
Safety Glasses	Abrasive Blast Hoods	Life Vest	
Goggles	Air Fed Respirators	Steel Toe Safety Shoes	Z41-1991
Face Shields	Other (specify below):	Hearing Protection (ANSI 3.19-1974)	
		Ear Plugs/Muffs	
		First Aid Kit for _____ Workers	1926.23 & .50
		Special Safety Guidelines	

COMMENTS

55

Safety is your most important responsibility—it starts with YOU!!

The following questions are but a sample of items that should be discussed in safety meetings. The author suggests at least 3 items from this list (or your own list) be directed at random employees to test their alertness after the safety meeting, just prior to entering the work area.

1. What was a topic on your JSA today?

2. What can you do today to insure your safety?

3. What does safety mean to you?

4. Safety starts with who?

5. Who is your supervisor?

6. When is the plant alarm tested?

7. Where do you go if an alarm sounds?

8. Did you inspect your safety harness today?

9. What does 100 percent tie off mean to you?

10. Where is the nearest eye wash station

11. What is heat stress?

12. How often should you drink water?

13. What does H_2S stand for?

DAILY SAFETY MEETING

LOCATION:	WEEK ENDING:
MEETING DATE:	
SPEAKER:	SUBJECT

ATTENDEES, PLEASE SIGN BELOW	
PRINTED NAME	SIGNATURE

If additional space is needed, please continue on a separate sheet.

*Should you be required to discuss an alternate subject, please identify and return signature sheet accordingly. Discuss the enclosed topic at your next available meeting.

Return this form to your area office—Attention: Safety Director.

DAILY SAFETY MEETING

LOCATION:	WEEK ENDING:
MEETING DATE:	
SPEAKER:	SUBJECT

ATTENDEES, PLEASE SIGN BELOW	
PRINTED NAME	SIGNATURE

If additional space is needed, please continue on a separate sheet.

*Should you be required to discuss an alternate subject, please identify and return signature sheet accordingly. Discuss the enclosed topic at your next available meeting.

Return this form to your area office—Attention: Safety Director.

DAILY SAFETY MEETING

LOCATION:	WEEK ENDING:
MEETING DATE:	
SPEAKER:	SUBJECT

ATTENDEES, PLEASE SIGN BELOW	
PRINTED NAME	SIGNATURE

If additional space is needed, please continue on a separate sheet.

*Should you be required to discuss an alternate subject, please identify and return signature sheet accordingly. Discuss the enclosed topic at your next available meeting.

Return this form to your area office—Attention: Safety Director.

DAILY SAFETY MEETING

LOCATION:	WEEK ENDING:
MEETING DATE:	
SPEAKER:	SUBJECT

ATTENDEES, PLEASE SIGN BELOW	
PRINTED NAME	SIGNATURE

If additional space is needed, please continue on a separate sheet.

*Should you be required to discuss an alternate subject, please identify and return signature sheet accordingly. Discuss the enclosed topic at your next available meeting.

Return this form to your area office—Attention: Safety Director.

DAILY SAFETY MEETING

LOCATION:		WEEK ENDING:
MEETING DATE:		
SPEAKER:		SUBJECT

ATTENDEES, PLEASE SIGN BELOW	
PRINTED NAME	SIGNATURE

If additional space is needed, please continue on a separate sheet.

*Should you be required to discuss an alternate subject, please identify and return signature sheet accordingly. Discuss the enclosed topic at your next available meeting.

Return this form to your area office—Attention: Safety Director.

DAILY SAFETY MEETING

LOCATION:	WEEK ENDING:
MEETING DATE:	
SPEAKER:	SUBJECT

ATTENDEES, PLEASE SIGN BELOW	
PRINTED NAME	SIGNATURE

If additional space is needed, please continue on a separate sheet.

*Should you be required to discuss an alternate subject, please identify and return signature sheet accordingly. Discuss the enclosed topic at your next available meeting.

Return this form to your area office--Attention: Safety Director.

DAILY SAFETY MEETING

LOCATION:	WEEK ENDING:
MEETING DATE:	
SPEAKER:	SUBJECT

ATTENDEES, PLEASE SIGN BELOW	
PRINTED NAME	SIGNATURE

If additional space is needed, please continue on a separate sheet.

*Should you be required to discuss an alternate subject, please identify and return signature sheet accordingly. Discuss the enclosed topic at your next available meeting.

Return this form to your area office—Attention: Safety Director.

DAILY SAFETY MEETING

LOCATION:		WEEK ENDING:
MEETING DATE:		
SPEAKER:		SUBJECT

ATTENDEES, PLEASE SIGN BELOW	
PRINTED NAME	SIGNATURE

If additional space is needed, please continue on a separate sheet.

*Should you be required to discuss an alternate subject, please identify and return signature sheet accordingly. Discuss the enclosed topic at your next available meeting.

Return this form to your area office—Attention: Safety Director.

DAILY SAFETY MEETING

LOCATION:	WEEK ENDING:
MEETING DATE:	
SPEAKER:	SUBJECT

ATTENDEES, PLEASE SIGN BELOW	
PRINTED NAME	SIGNATURE

If additional space is needed, please continue on a separate sheet.

*Should you be required to discuss an alternate subject, please identify and return signature sheet accordingly. Discuss the enclosed topic at your next available meeting.

Return this form to your area office—Attention: Safety Director.

DAILY SAFETY MEETING

LOCATION:	WEEK ENDING:
MEETING DATE:	
SPEAKER:	SUBJECT

ATTENDEES, PLEASE SIGN BELOW	
PRINTED NAME	SIGNATURE

If additional space is needed, please continue on a separate sheet.

*Should you be required to discuss an alternate subject, please identify and return signature sheet accordingly. Discuss the enclosed topic at your next available meeting.

Return this form to your area office–Attention: Safety Director.

DAILY SAFETY MEETING

LOCATION:	WEEK ENDING:
MEETING DATE:	
SPEAKER:	SUBJECT

ATTENDEES, PLEASE SIGN BELOW	
PRINTED NAME	SIGNATURE

If additional space is needed, please continue on a separate sheet.

*Should you be required to discuss an alternate subject, please identify and return signature sheet accordingly. Discuss the enclosed topic at your next available meeting.

Return this form to your area office—Attention: Safety Director.

DAILY SAFETY MEETING

LOCATION:		WEEK ENDING:
MEETING DATE:		
SPEAKER:		SUBJECT

ATTENDEES, PLEASE SIGN BELOW	
PRINTED NAME	SIGNATURE

If additional space is needed, please continue on a separate sheet.

*Should you be required to discuss an alternate subject, please identify and return signature sheet accordingly. Discuss the enclosed topic at your next available meeting.

Return this form to your area office—Attention: Safety Director.

DAILY SAFETY MEETING

LOCATION:	WEEK ENDING:
MEETING DATE:	
SPEAKER:	SUBJECT

ATTENDEES, PLEASE SIGN BELOW	
PRINTED NAME	SIGNATURE

If additional space is needed, please continue on a separate sheet.

*Should you be required to discuss an alternate subject, please identify and return signature sheet accordingly. Discuss the enclosed topic at your next available meeting.

Return this form to your area office—Attention: Safety Director.

DAILY SAFETY MEETING

LOCATION:	WEEK ENDING:
MEETING DATE:	
SPEAKER:	SUBJECT

ATTENDEES, PLEASE SIGN BELOW	
PRINTED NAME	SIGNATURE

If additional space is needed, please continue on a separate sheet.

*Should you be required to discuss an alternate subject, please identify and return signature sheet accordingly. Discuss the enclosed topic at your next available meeting.

Return this form to your area office—Attention: Safety Director.

DAILY SAFETY MEETING

LOCATION:	WEEK ENDING:
MEETING DATE:	
SPEAKER:	SUBJECT

ATTENDEES, PLEASE SIGN BELOW	
PRINTED NAME	SIGNATURE

If additional space is needed, please continue on a separate sheet.

*Should you be required to discuss an alternate subject, please identify and return signature sheet accordingly. Discuss the enclosed topic at your next available meeting.

Return this form to your area office—Attention: Safety Director.

Contractors and owners should maintain awareness of heat related stress.

90 °F (32 °C) to 109 °F (42 °C)

Consult management if working at temperatures above 110 °F (43 °C)

> Minimize exposure to the sun
>
> Wear lightweight clothing if possible
>
> Pace yourself and take short, frequent breaks
>
> Drink plenty of water

Symptoms generally fall under 3 classifications:
- Heat cramps
- Heat exhaustion
- Heat stroke

A heat stroke is serious— call your local emergency hotline!

HYDRATION LOG

Date starting:

Supervisor:

Customer:

Superintendent:

Each employee must consume a minimum of 8 oz. of water per hour.

Heat Stress	Signs & Symptoms	Treatment
Cramps (mild)	Sweating, irritable	Rest, drink fluids
Exhaustion (moderate)	Weakness, pale	Cool body with fluids, fan
Stroke (severe)	Hot, dry skin	As above, no clothing

EMPLOYEE NAME	8 am	9 am	10 am	11 am	12 pm	1 pm	2 pm	3 pm	4 pm	5 pm	6 pm	NOTES

HYDRATION LOG

Date starting:

Supervisor:

Customer:

Superintendent:

Each employee must consume a minimum of 8 oz. of water per hour.

	Heat Stress	Signs & Symptoms	Treatment
	Cramps (mild)	Sweating, irritable	Rest, drink fluids
	Exhaustion (moderate)	Weakness, pale	Cool body with fluids, fan
	Stroke (severe)	Hot, dry skin	As above, no clothing

EMPLOYEE NAME	8 am	9 am	10 am	11 am	12 pm	1 pm	2 pm	3 pm	4 pm	5 pm	6 pm

NOTES

HYDRATION LOG

Date starting:

Supervisor:

Customer:

Superintendent:

Each employee must consume a minimum of 8 oz. of water per hour.

Heat Stress	Signs & Symptoms	Treatment
Cramps (mild)	Sweating, irritable	Rest, drink fluids
Exhaustion (moderate)	Weakness, pale	Cool body with fluids, fan
Stroke (severe)	Hot, dry skin	As above, no clothing

EMPLOYEE NAME	8 am	9 am	10 am	11 am	12 pm	1 pm	2 pm	3 pm	4 pm	5 pm	6 pm

NOTES

HYDRATION LOG

Date starting:

Supervisor:

Customer:

Superintendent:

Each employee must consume a minimum of 8 oz. of water per hour.

Heat Stress	Signs & Symptoms	Treatment
Cramps (mild)	Sweating, irritable	Rest, drink fluids
Exhaustion (moderate)	Weakness, pale	Cool body with fluids, fan
Stroke (severe)	Hot, dry skin	As above, no clothing

EMPLOYEE NAME	8 am	9 am	10 am	11 am	12 pm	1 pm	2 pm	3 pm	4 pm	5 pm	6 pm

NOTES

HYDRATION LOG

Date starting:

Supervisor:

Customer:

Superintendent:

Each employee must consume a minimum of 8 oz. of water per hour.

	Heat Stress	Signs & Symptoms	Treatment
	Cramps (mild)	Sweating, irritable	Rest, drink fluids
	Exhaustion (moderate)	Weakness, pale	Cool body with fluids, fan
	Stroke (severe)	Hot, dry skin	As above, no clothing

EMPLOYEE NAME	8 am	9 am	10 am	11 am	12 pm	1 pm	2 pm	3 pm	4 pm	5 pm	6 pm

NOTES

HYDRATION LOG

Date starting:

Supervisor:

Customer:

Superintendent:

Each employee must consume a minimum of 8 oz. of water per hour.

Heat Stress	Signs & Symptoms	Treatment
Cramps (mild)	Sweating, irritable	Rest, drink fluids
Exhaustion (moderate)	Weakness, pale	Cool body with fluids, fan
Stroke (severe)	Hot, dry skin	As above, no clothing

EMPLOYEE NAME	8 am	9 am	10 am	11 am	12 pm	1 pm	2 pm	3 pm	4 pm	5 pm	6 pm

NOTES

HYDRATION LOG

Date starting:

Supervisor:

Customer:

Superintendent:

Each employee must consume a minimum of 8 oz. of water per hour.

Heat Stress	Signs & Symptoms	Treatment
Cramps (mild)	Sweating, irritable	Rest, drink fluids
Exhaustion (moderate)	Weakness, pale	Cool body with fluids, fan
Stroke (severe)	Hot, dry skin	As above, no clothing

EMPLOYEE NAME	NOTES	8 am	9 am	10 am	11 am	12 pm	1 pm	2 pm	3 pm	4 pm	5 pm	6 pm

HYDRATION LOG

Date starting:	
Supervisor:	
Customer:	
Superintendent:	

Each employee must consume a minimum of 8 oz. of water per hour.

	Heat Stress	Signs & Symptoms	Treatment
	Cramps (mild)	Sweating, irritable	Rest, drink fluids
	Exhaustion (moderate)	Weakness, pale	Cool body with fluids; fan
	Stroke (severe)	Hot, dry skin	As above, no clothing

EMPLOYEE NAME	8 am	9 am	10 am	11 am	12 pm	1 pm	2 pm	3 pm	4 pm	5 pm	6 pm

NOTES

HYDRATION LOG

Date starting:											
Supervisor:											
Customer:											

Each employee must consume a minimum of 8 oz. of water per hour.

	Heat Stress	Signs & Symptoms	Treatment
	Cramps (mild)	Sweating, irritable	Rest, drink fluids
	Exhaustion (moderate)	Weakness, pale	Cool body with fluids, fan
	Stroke (severe)	Hot, dry skin	As above, no clothing

Superintendent:

EMPLOYEE NAME	8 am	9 am	10 am	11 am	12 pm	1 pm	2 pm	3 pm	4 pm	5 pm	6 pm

NOTES

HYDRATION LOG

Date starting:

Supervisor:

Customer:

Superintendent:

Each employee must consume a minimum of 8 oz. of water per hour.

Heat Stress	Signs & Symptoms	Treatment
Cramps (mild)	Sweating, irritable	Rest, drink fluids
Exhaustion (moderate)	Weakness, pale	Cool body with fluids, fan
Stroke (severe)	Hot, dry skin	As above, no clothing

EMPLOYEE NAME	8 am	9 am	10 am	11 am	12 pm	1 pm	2 pm	3 pm	4 pm	5 pm	6 pm

NOTES

HYDRATION LOG

Date starting:

Supervisor:

Customer:

Superintendent:

Each employee must consume a minimum of 8 oz. of water per hour.

	Heat Stress	Signs & Symptoms	Treatment
	Cramps (mild)	Sweating, irritable	Rest, drink fluids
	Exhaustion (moderate)	Weakness, pale	Cool body with fluids, fan
	Stroke (severe)	Hot, dry skin	As above, no clothing

EMPLOYEE NAME	8 am	9 am	10 am	11 am	12 pm	1 pm	2 pm	3 pm	4 pm	5 pm	6 pm

NOTES

SAFETY HARNESS AND LANYARD INSPECTION

FULL BODY HARNESS AND LANYARD INSPECTION CRITERIA

HARNESS

WEBBING	YES	NO	NOTES
Cuts			
Fraying			
Abrasions			
Damaged Stitching			
Chemical Exposure			
Burns			

HARDWARE	YES	NO	NOTES
Deformed			
Corrosion			
Rust			
Chemical Exposure			

LANYARD

DOUBLE LATCH HOOK	YES	NO	NOTES
Gate works freely			

DOUBLE LOCK WORKS CORRECTLY	YES	NO	NOTES
Deformed			
Corrosion			
Rust			
Chemical Exposure			

WEBBING	YES	NO	NOTES
Cuts			
Fraying			
Abrasions			
Damaged Stitching			
Chemical Exposure			
Burns			

SHOCK ABSORBING MECHANISM

	YES	NO	NOTES
Harness has sustained a shock load			
Lanyard has sustained a shock load			

NOTE: Note: Any harness or lanyard that has been depolyed (sustained a shock load) should be immediately removed from service.

COMMENTS

FULL BODY HARNESS AND LANYARD INSPECTION CRITERIA

HARNESS			
WEBBING	**YES**	**NO**	**NOTES**
Cuts			
Fraying			
Abrasions			
Damaged Stitching			
Chemical Exposure			
Burns			
HARDWARE	**YES**	**NO**	**NOTES**
Deformed			
Corrosion			
Rust			
Chemical Exposure			
LANYARD			
DOUBLE LATCH HOOK	**YES**	**NO**	**NOTES**
Gate works freely			
DOUBLE LOCK WORKS CORRECTLY	**YES**	**NO**	**NOTES**
Deformed			
Corrosion			
Rust			
Chemical Exposure			
WEBBING	**YES**	**NO**	**NOTES**
Cuts			
Fraying			
Abrasions			
Damaged Stitching			
Chemical Exposure			
Burns			
SHOCK ABSORBING MECHANISM			
	YES	**NO**	**NOTES**
Harness has sustained a shock load			
Lanyard has sustained a shock load			

NOTE: Note: Any harness or lanyard that has been depolyed (sustained a shock load) should be immediately removed from service.

COMMENTS

FULL BODY HARNESS AND LANYARD INSPECTION CRITERIA

HARNESS

WEBBING	YES	NO	NOTES
Cuts			
Fraying			
Abrasions			
Damaged Stitching			
Chemical Exposure			
Burns			

HARDWARE	YES	NO	NOTES
Deformed			
Corrosion			
Rust			
Chemical Exposure			

LANYARD

DOUBLE LATCH HOOK	YES	NO	NOTES
Gate works freely			

DOUBLE LOCK WORKS CORRECTLY	YES	NO	NOTES
Deformed			
Corrosion			
Rust			
Chemical Exposure			

WEBBING	YES	NO	NOTES
Cuts			
Fraying			
Abrasions			
Damaged Stitching			
Chemical Exposure			
Burns			

SHOCK ABSORBING MECHANISM

	YES	NO	NOTES
Harness has sustained a shock load			
Lanyard has sustained a shock load			

NOTE: Note: Any harness or lanyard that has been depolyed (sustained a shock load) should be immediately removed from service.

COMMENTS

FULL BODY HARNESS AND LANYARD INSPECTION CRITERIA

HARNESS

WEBBING	YES	NO	NOTES
Cuts			
Fraying			
Abrasions			
Damaged Stitching			
Chemical Exposure			
Burns			
HARDWARE	**YES**	**NO**	**NOTES**
Deformed			
Corrosion			
Rust			
Chemical Exposure			

LANYARD

DOUBLE LATCH HOOK	YES	NO	NOTES
Gate works freely			
DOUBLE LOCK WORKS CORRECTLY	**YES**	**NO**	**NOTES**
Deformed			
Corrosion			
Rust			
Chemical Exposure			
WEBBING	**YES**	**NO**	**NOTES**
Cuts			
Fraying			
Abrasions			
Damaged Stitching			
Chemical Exposure			
Burns			

SHOCK ABSORBING MECHANISM

	YES	NO	NOTES
Harness has sustained a shock load			
Lanyard has sustained a shock load			

NOTE: Note: Any harness or lanyard that has been depolyed (sustained a shock load) should be immediately removed from service.

COMMENTS

FULL BODY HARNESS AND LANYARD INSPECTION CRITERIA

HARNESS			
WEBBING	**YES**	**NO**	**NOTES**
Cuts			
Fraying			
Abrasions			
Damaged Stitching			
Chemical Exposure			
Burns			
HARDWARE	**YES**	**NO**	**NOTES**
Deformed			
Corrosion			
Rust			
Chemical Exposure			

LANYARD			
DOUBLE LATCH HOOK	**YES**	**NO**	**NOTES**
Gate works freely			
DOUBLE LOCK WORKS CORRECTLY	**YES**	**NO**	**NOTES**
Deformed			
Corrosion			
Rust			
Chemical Exposure			
WEBBING	**YES**	**NO**	**NOTES**
Cuts			
Fraying			
Abrasions			
Damaged Stitching			
Chemical Exposure			
Burns			

SHOCK ABSORBING MECHANISM			
	YES	**NO**	**NOTES**
Harness has sustained a shock load			
Lanyard has sustained a shock load			

NOTE: Note: Any harness or lanyard that has been depolyed (sustained a shock load) should be immediately removed from service.

COMMENTS

FULL BODY HARNESS AND LANYARD INSPECTION CRITERIA

HARNESS

WEBBING	YES	NO	NOTES
Cuts			
Fraying			
Abrasions			
Damaged Stitching			
Chemical Exposure			
Burns			
HARDWARE	YES	NO	NOTES
Deformed			
Corrosion			
Rust			
Chemical Exposure			

LANYARD

DOUBLE LATCH HOOK	YES	NO	NOTES
Gate works freely			
DOUBLE LOCK WORKS CORRECTLY	YES	NO	NOTES
Deformed			
Corrosion			
Rust			
Chemical Exposure			
WEBBING	YES	NO	NOTES
Cuts			
Fraying			
Abrasions			
Damaged Stitching			
Chemical Exposure			
Burns			

SHOCK ABSORBING MECHANISM

	YES	NO	NOTES
Harness has sustained a shock load			
Lanyard has sustained a shock load			

NOTE: Note: Any harness or lanyard that has been depolyed (sustained a shock load) should be immediately removed from service.

COMMENTS

FULL BODY HARNESS AND LANYARD INSPECTION CRITERIA

HARNESS			
WEBBING	YES	NO	NOTES
Cuts			
Fraying			
Abrasions			
Damaged Stitching			
Chemical Exposure			
Burns			
HARDWARE	YES	NO	NOTES
Deformed			
Corrosion			
Rust			
Chemical Exposure			
LANYARD			
DOUBLE LATCH HOOK	YES	NO	NOTES
Gate works freely			
DOUBLE LOCK WORKS CORRECTLY	YES	NO	NOTES
Deformed			
Corrosion			
Rust			
Chemical Exposure			
WEBBING	YES	NO	NOTES
Cuts			
Fraying			
Abrasions			
Damaged Stitching			
Chemical Exposure			
Burns			
SHOCK ABSORBING MECHANISM			
	YES	NO	NOTES
Harness has sustained a shock load			
Lanyard has sustained a shock load			

NOTE: Note: Any harness or lanyard that has been depolyed (sustained a shock load) should be immediately removed from service.

COMMENTS

FULL BODY HARNESS AND LANYARD INSPECTION CRITERIA

HARNESS			
WEBBING	**YES**	**NO**	**NOTES**
Cuts			
Fraying			
Abrasions			
Damaged Stitching			
Chemical Exposure			
Burns			
HARDWARE	**YES**	**NO**	**NOTES**
Deformed			
Corrosion			
Rust			
Chemical Exposure			

LANYARD			
DOUBLE LATCH HOOK	**YES**	**NO**	**NOTES**
Gate works freely			
DOUBLE LOCK WORKS CORRECTLY	**YES**	**NO**	**NOTES**
Deformed			
Corrosion			
Rust			
Chemical Exposure			
WEBBING	**YES**	**NO**	**NOTES**
Cuts			
Fraying			
Abrasions			
Damaged Stitching			
Chemical Exposure			
Burns			

SHOCK ABSORBING MECHANISM			
	YES	**NO**	**NOTES**
Harness has sustained a shock load			
Lanyard has sustained a shock load			

NOTE: Note: Any harness or lanyard that has been depolyed (sustained a shock load) should be immediately removed from service.

COMMENTS

FULL BODY HARNESS AND LANYARD INSPECTION CRITERIA

HARNESS			
WEBBING	**YES**	**NO**	**NOTES**
Cuts			
Fraying			
Abrasions			
Damaged Stitching			
Chemical Exposure			
Burns			
HARDWARE	**YES**	**NO**	**NOTES**
Deformed			
Corrosion			
Rust			
Chemical Exposure			

LANYARD			
DOUBLE LATCH HOOK	**YES**	**NO**	**NOTES**
Gate works freely			
DOUBLE LOCK WORKS CORRECTLY	**YES**	**NO**	**NOTES**
Deformed			
Corrosion			
Rust			
Chemical Exposure			
WEBBING	**YES**	**NO**	**NOTES**
Cuts			
Fraying			
Abrasions			
Damaged Stitching			
Chemical Exposure			
Burns			

SHOCK ABSORBING MECHANISM			
	YES	**NO**	**NOTES**
Harness has sustained a shock load			
Lanyard has sustained a shock load			

NOTE: Note: Any harness or lanyard that has been depolyed (sustained a shock load) should be immediately removed from service.

COMMENTS

FULL BODY HARNESS AND LANYARD INSPECTION CRITERIA

HARNESS			
WEBBING	**YES**	**NO**	**NOTES**
Cuts			
Fraying			
Abrasions			
Damaged Stitching			
Chemical Exposure			
Burns			
HARDWARE	**YES**	**NO**	**NOTES**
Deformed			
Corrosion			
Rust			
Chemical Exposure			

LANYARD			
DOUBLE LATCH HOOK	**YES**	**NO**	**NOTES**
Gate works freely			
DOUBLE LOCK WORKS CORRECTLY	**YES**	**NO**	**NOTES**
Deformed			
Corrosion			
Rust			
Chemical Exposure			
WEBBING	**YES**	**NO**	**NOTES**
Cuts			
Fraying			
Abrasions			
Damaged Stitching			
Chemical Exposure			
Burns			

SHOCK ABSORBING MECHANISM			
	YES	**NO**	**NOTES**
Harness has sustained a shock load			
Lanyard has sustained a shock load			

NOTE: Note: Any harness or lanyard that has been depolyed (sustained a shock load) should be immediately removed from service.

COMMENTS

FULL BODY HARNESS AND LANYARD INSPECTION CRITERIA

HARNESS			
WEBBING	**YES**	**NO**	**NOTES**
Cuts			
Fraying			
Abrasions			
Damaged Stitching			
Chemical Exposure			
Burns			
HARDWARE	**YES**	**NO**	**NOTES**
Deformed			
Corrosion			
Rust			
Chemical Exposure			
LANYARD			
DOUBLE LATCH HOOK	**YES**	**NO**	**NOTES**
Gate works freely			
DOUBLE LOCK WORKS CORRECTLY	**YES**	**NO**	**NOTES**
Deformed			
Corrosion			
Rust			
Chemical Exposure			
WEBBING	**YES**	**NO**	**NOTES**
Cuts			
Fraying			
Abrasions			
Damaged Stitching			
Chemical Exposure			
Burns			
SHOCK ABSORBING MECHANISM			
	YES	**NO**	**NOTES**
Harness has sustained a shock load			
Lanyard has sustained a shock load			

NOTE: Note: Any harness or lanyard that has been depolyed (sustained a shock load) should be immediately removed from service.

COMMENTS

FULL BODY HARNESS AND LANYARD INSPECTION CRITERIA

HARNESS				
WEBBING	YES	NO	NOTES	
Cuts				
Fraying				
Abrasions				
Damaged Stitching				
Chemical Exposure				
Burns				
HARDWARE	YES	NO	NOTES	
Deformed				
Corrosion				
Rust				
Chemical Exposure				

LANYARD				
DOUBLE LATCH HOOK	YES	NO	NOTES	
Gate works freely				
DOUBLE LOCK WORKS CORRECTLY	YES	NO	NOTES	
Deformed				
Corrosion				
Rust				
Chemical Exposure				
WEBBING	YES	NO	NOTES	
Cuts				
Fraying				
Abrasions				
Damaged Stitching				
Chemical Exposure				
Burns				

SHOCK ABSORBING MECHANISM				
	YES	NO	NOTES	
Harness has sustained a shock load				
Lanyard has sustained a shock load				

NOTE: Note: Any harness or lanyard that has been depolyed (sustained a shock load) should be immediately removed from service.

COMMENTS

FULL BODY HARNESS AND LANYARD INSPECTION CRITERIA

HARNESS

WEBBING	YES	NO	NOTES
Cuts			
Fraying			
Abrasions			
Damaged Stitching			
Chemical Exposure			
Burns			
HARDWARE	**YES**	**NO**	**NOTES**
Deformed			
Corrosion			
Rust			
Chemical Exposure			

LANYARD

DOUBLE LATCH HOOK	YES	NO	NOTES
Gate works freely			
DOUBLE LOCK WORKS CORRECTLY	**YES**	**NO**	**NOTES**
Deformed			
Corrosion			
Rust			
Chemical Exposure			
WEBBING	**YES**	**NO**	**NOTES**
Cuts			
Fraying			
Abrasions			
Damaged Stitching			
Chemical Exposure			
Burns			

SHOCK ABSORBING MECHANISM

	YES	NO	NOTES
Harness has sustained a shock load			
Lanyard has sustained a shock load			

NOTE: Note: Any harness or lanyard that has been depolyed (sustained a shock load) should be immediately removed from service.

COMMENTS

FULL BODY HARNESS AND LANYARD INSPECTION CRITERIA

HARNESS

WEBBING	YES	NO	NOTES
Cuts			
Fraying			
Abrasions			
Damaged Stitching			
Chemical Exposure			
Burns			

HARDWARE	YES	NO	NOTES
Deformed			
Corrosion			
Rust			
Chemical Exposure			

LANYARD

DOUBLE LATCH HOOK	YES	NO	NOTES
Gate works freely			

DOUBLE LOCK WORKS CORRECTLY	YES	NO	NOTES
Deformed			
Corrosion			
Rust			
Chemical Exposure			

WEBBING	YES	NO	NOTES
Cuts			
Fraying			
Abrasions			
Damaged Stitching			
Chemical Exposure			
Burns			

SHOCK ABSORBING MECHANISM

	YES	NO	NOTES
Harness has sustained a shock load			
Lanyard has sustained a shock load			

NOTE: Note: Any harness or lanyard that has been depolyed (sustained a shock load) should be immediately removed from service.

COMMENTS

FULL BODY HARNESS AND LANYARD INSPECTION CRITERIA

HARNESS			
WEBBING	**YES**	**NO**	**NOTES**
Cuts			
Fraying			
Abrasions			
Damaged Stitching			
Chemical Exposure			
Burns			
HARDWARE	**YES**	**NO**	**NOTES**
Deformed			
Corrosion			
Rust			
Chemical Exposure			

LANYARD			
DOUBLE LATCH HOOK	**YES**	**NO**	**NOTES**
Gate works freely			
DOUBLE LOCK WORKS CORRECTLY	**YES**	**NO**	**NOTES**
Deformed			
Corrosion			
Rust			
Chemical Exposure			
WEBBING	**YES**	**NO**	**NOTES**
Cuts			
Fraying			
Abrasions			
Damaged Stitching			
Chemical Exposure			
Burns			

SHOCK ABSORBING MECHANISM			
	YES	**NO**	**NOTES**
Harness has sustained a shock load			
Lanyard has sustained a shock load			

NOTE: Note: Any harness or lanyard that has been depolyed (sustained a shock load) should be immediately removed from service.

COMMENTS

ATMOSPHERE MONITORING INSTRUMENT CALIBRATION LOG

ATMOSPHERE MONITORING INSTRUMENT CALIBRATION LOG

Unit Model Number:			Unit Brand Name:	
Unit Serial Number:			Purchase Date:	
Speaker:			Subject:	
Calibration Gas Composition	Hydrogen Sulfide (H$_2$S)	25 ppm		
	Carbon Monoxide (CO)	100 ppm		
	Pentane (equivalent)	30% LEL		
	Oxygen (O$_2$)	18.0%		
		Lot #		

Date	Check action that applies		Calibrator/Tester Name
	Bump Test	Recalibration	
	☐	☐	
	☐	☐	
	☐	☐	
	☐	☐	
	☐	☐	
	☐	☐	
	☐	☐	
	☐	☐	
	☐	☐	
	☐	☐	
	☐	☐	
	☐	☐	
	☐	☐	
	☐	☐	
	☐	☐	
	☐	☐	
	☐	☐	
	☐	☐	
	☐	☐	
	☐	☐	
	☐	☐	
	☐	☐	
	☐	☐	
	☐	☐	
	☐	☐	
	☐	☐	
	☐	☐	
	☐	☐	
	☐	☐	

ATMOSPHERE MONITORING INSTRUMENT CALIBRATION LOG

Unit Model Number:		Unit Brand Name:	
Unit Serial Number:		Purchase Date:	
Speaker:		Subject:	

Calibration Gas Composition	Hydrogen Sulfide (H$_2$S)	25 ppm	
	Carbon Monoxide (CO)	100 ppm	
	Pentane (equivalent)	30% LEL	
	Oxygen (O$_2$)	18.0%	
		Lot #	

Date	Check action that applies		Calibrator/Tester Name
	Bump Test	Recalibration	
	☐	☐	
	☐	☐	
	☐	☐	
	☐	☐	
	☐	☐	
	☐	☐	
	☐	☐	
	☐	☐	
	☐	☐	
	☐	☐	
	☐	☐	
	☐	☐	
	☐	☐	
	☐	☐	
	☐	☐	
	☐	☐	
	☐	☐	
	☐	☐	
	☐	☐	
	☐	☐	
	☐	☐	
	☐	☐	
	☐	☐	
	☐	☐	
	☐	☐	
	☐	☐	
	☐	☐	
	☐	☐	

ATMOSPHERE MONITORING INSTRUMENT CALIBRATION LOG

Unit Model Number:		Unit Brand Name:	
Unit Serial Number:		Purchase Date:	
Speaker:		Subject:	
Calibration Gas Composition	Hydrogen Sulfide (H$_2$S)	25 ppm	
	Carbon Monoxide (CO)	100 ppm	
	Pentane (equivalent)	30% LEL	
	Oxygen (O$_2$)	18.0%	
		Lot #	

Date	Check action that applies		Calibrator/Tester Name
	Bump Test	Recalibration	
	☐	☐	
	☐	☐	
	☐	☐	
	☐	☐	
	☐	☐	
	☐	☐	
	☐	☐	
	☐	☐	
	☐	☐	
	☐	☐	
	☐	☐	
	☐	☐	
	☐	☐	
	☐	☐	
	☐	☐	
	☐	☐	
	☐	☐	
	☐	☐	
	☐	☐	
	☐	☐	
	☐	☐	
	☐	☐	
	☐	☐	
	☐	☐	
	☐	☐	
	☐	☐	
	☐	☐	
	☐	☐	

ATMOSPHERE MONITORING INSTRUMENT CALIBRATION LOG

Unit Model Number:		Unit Brand Name:	
Unit Serial Number:		Purchase Date:	
Speaker:		Subject:	

Calibration Gas Composition	Hydrogen Sulfide (H$_2$S)	25 ppm	
	Carbon Monoxide (CO)	100 ppm	
	Pentane (equivalent)	30% LEL	
	Oxygen (O$_2$)	18.0%	
		Lot #	

Date	Check action that applies		Calibrator/Tester Name
	Bump Test	Recalibration	
	☐	☐	
	☐	☐	
	☐	☐	
	☐	☐	
	☐	☐	
	☐	☐	
	☐	☐	
	☐	☐	
	☐	☐	
	☐	☐	
	☐	☐	
	☐	☐	
	☐	☐	
	☐	☐	
	☐	☐	
	☐	☐	
	☐	☐	
	☐	☐	
	☐	☐	
	☐	☐	
	☐	☐	
	☐	☐	
	☐	☐	
	☐	☐	
	☐	☐	
	☐	☐	
	☐	☐	
	☐	☐	
	☐	☐	
	☐	☐	

ATMOSPHERE MONITORING INSTRUMENT CALIBRATION LOG

Unit Model Number:		Unit Brand Name:	
Unit Serial Number:		Purchase Date:	
Speaker:		Subject:	

Calibration Gas Composition	Hydrogen Sulfide (H_2S)	25 ppm	
	Carbon Monoxide (CO)	100 ppm	
	Pentane (equivalent)	30% LEL	
	Oxygen (O_2)	18.0%	
		Lot #	

Date	Check action that applies		Calibrator/Tester Name
	Bump Test	Recalibration	
	☐	☐	
	☐	☐	
	☐	☐	
	☐	☐	
	☐	☐	
	☐	☐	
	☐	☐	
	☐	☐	
	☐	☐	
	☐	☐	
	☐	☐	
	☐	☐	
	☐	☐	
	☐	☐	
	☐	☐	
	☐	☐	
	☐	☐	
	☐	☐	
	☐	☐	
	☐	☐	
	☐	☐	
	☐	☐	
	☐	☐	
	☐	☐	
	☐	☐	
	☐	☐	
	☐	☐	
	☐	☐	

ATMOSPHERE MONITORING INSTRUMENT CALIBRATION LOG

Unit Model Number:		Unit Brand Name:
Unit Serial Number:		Purchase Date:
Speaker:		Subject:

Calibration Gas Composition	Hydrogen Sulfide (H$_2$S)	25 ppm	
	Carbon Monoxide (CO)	100 ppm	
	Pentane (equivalent)	30% LEL	
	Oxygen (O$_2$)	18.0%	
		Lot #	

Date	Check action that applies		Calibrator/Tester Name
	Bump Test	Recalibration	
	☐	☐	
	☐	☐	
	☐	☐	
	☐	☐	
	☐	☐	
	☐	☐	
	☐	☐	
	☐	☐	
	☐	☐	
	☐	☐	
	☐	☐	
	☐	☐	
	☐	☐	
	☐	☐	
	☐	☐	
	☐	☐	
	☐	☐	
	☐	☐	
	☐	☐	
	☐	☐	
	☐	☐	
	☐	☐	
	☐	☐	
	☐	☐	
	☐	☐	
	☐	☐	
	☐	☐	
	☐	☐	

ATMOSPHERE MONITORING INSTRUMENT CALIBRATION LOG

Unit Model Number:		Unit Brand Name:	
Unit Serial Number:		Purchase Date:	
Speaker:		Subject:	

Calibration Gas Composition			
	Hydrogen Sulfide (H_2S)	25 ppm	
	Carbon Monoxide (CO)	100 ppm	
	Pentane (equivalent)	30% LEL	
	Oxygen (O_2)	18.0%	
		Lot #	

Date	Check action that applies		Calibrator/Tester Name
	Bump Test	Recalibration	
	☐	☐	
	☐	☐	
	☐	☐	
	☐	☐	
	☐	☐	
	☐	☐	
	☐	☐	
	☐	☐	
	☐	☐	
	☐	☐	
	☐	☐	
	☐	☐	
	☐	☐	
	☐	☐	
	☐	☐	
	☐	☐	
	☐	☐	
	☐	☐	
	☐	☐	
	☐	☐	
	☐	☐	
	☐	☐	
	☐	☐	
	☐	☐	
	☐	☐	
	☐	☐	
	☐	☐	
	☐	☐	

ATMOSPHERE MONITORING INSTRUMENT CALIBRATION LOG

Unit Model Number:		Unit Brand Name:	
Unit Serial Number:		Purchase Date:	
Speaker:		Subject:	
Calibration Gas Composition	Hydrogen Sulfide (H_2S)	25 ppm	
	Carbon Monoxide (CO)	100 ppm	
	Pentane (equivalent)	30% LEL	
	Oxygen (O_2)	18.0%	
		Lot #	

Date	Check action that applies		Calibrator/Tester Name
	Bump Test	Recalibration	
	☐	☐	
	☐	☐	
	☐	☐	
	☐	☐	
	☐	☐	
	☐	☐	
	☐	☐	
	☐	☐	
	☐	☐	
	☐	☐	
	☐	☐	
	☐	☐	
	☐	☐	
	☐	☐	
	☐	☐	
	☐	☐	
	☐	☐	
	☐	☐	
	☐	☐	
	☐	☐	
	☐	☐	
	☐	☐	
	☐	☐	
	☐	☐	
	☐	☐	
	☐	☐	
	☐	☐	
	☐	☐	

ATMOSPHERE MONITORING INSTRUMENT CALIBRATION LOG

Unit Model Number:		Unit Brand Name:	
Unit Serial Number:		Purchase Date:	
Speaker:		Subject:	

Calibration Gas Composition	Hydrogen Sulfide (H_2S)	25 ppm	
	Carbon Monoxide (CO)	100 ppm	
	Pentane (equivalent)	30% LEL	
	Oxygen (O_2)	18.0%	
		Lot #	

Date	Check action that applies		Calibrator/Tester Name
	Bump Test	Recalibration	
	☐	☐	
	☐	☐	
	☐	☐	
	☐	☐	
	☐	☐	
	☐	☐	
	☐	☐	
	☐	☐	
	☐	☐	
	☐	☐	
	☐	☐	
	☐	☐	
	☐	☐	
	☐	☐	
	☐	☐	
	☐	☐	
	☐	☐	
	☐	☐	
	☐	☐	
	☐	☐	
	☐	☐	
	☐	☐	
	☐	☐	
	☐	☐	
	☐	☐	
	☐	☐	
	☐	☐	
	☐	☐	
	☐	☐	

ATMOSPHERE MONITORING INSTRUMENT CALIBRATION LOG

Unit Model Number:		Unit Brand Name:		
Unit Serial Number:		Purchase Date:		
Speaker:		Subject:		
Calibration Gas Composition	Hydrogen Sulfide (H$_2$S)	25 ppm		
	Carbon Monoxide (CO)	100 ppm		
	Pentane (equivalent)	30% LEL		
	Oxygen (O$_2$)	18.0%		
		Lot #		

Date	Check action that applies		Calibrator/Tester Name
	Bump Test	Recalibration	
	☐	☐	
	☐	☐	
	☐	☐	
	☐	☐	
	☐	☐	
	☐	☐	
	☐	☐	
	☐	☐	
	☐	☐	
	☐	☐	
	☐	☐	
	☐	☐	
	☐	☐	
	☐	☐	
	☐	☐	
	☐	☐	
	☐	☐	
	☐	☐	
	☐	☐	
	☐	☐	
	☐	☐	
	☐	☐	
	☐	☐	
	☐	☐	
	☐	☐	
	☐	☐	
	☐	☐	
	☐	☐	

ATMOSPHERE MONITORING INSTRUMENT CALIBRATION LOG

Unit Model Number:			Unit Brand Name:	
Unit Serial Number:			Purchase Date:	
Speaker:			Subject:	
Calibration Gas Composition	Hydrogen Sulfide (H$_2$S)		25 ppm	
	Carbon Monoxide (CO)		100 ppm	
	Pentane (equivalent)		30% LEL	
	Oxygen (O$_2$)		18.0%	
			Lot #	

Date	Check action that applies		Calibrator/Tester Name
	Bump Test	Recalibration	
	☐	☐	
	☐	☐	
	☐	☐	
	☐	☐	
	☐	☐	
	☐	☐	
	☐	☐	
	☐	☐	
	☐	☐	
	☐	☐	
	☐	☐	
	☐	☐	
	☐	☐	
	☐	☐	
	☐	☐	
	☐	☐	
	☐	☐	
	☐	☐	
	☐	☐	
	☐	☐	
	☐	☐	
	☐	☐	
	☐	☐	
	☐	☐	
	☐	☐	
	☐	☐	
	☐	☐	
	☐	☐	

EMPLOYEE HOUSEKEEPING JOB SITE AUDIT

EMPLOYEE HOUSEKEEPING DAILY AUDIT

Job #:	Month Ending:
Job Name:	Location:
Audit By:	Superintendent:

General requirements: This daily audit form is to be used as a tool alongside our JSA to enhance awareness of potential job site hazards and encourage every employee to have the confidence, courage, and ability to perform basic audits.

These audits will be performed two (2) times daily. They will be maintained and, upon request, made available for inspection.

	YES	NO	Corrective Action Taken
Trash—all trash—removed from work area (Insure trash is segregated by type; hazardous vs. non-hazardous)			
Is there unused or old barricade tape in the area?			
Are there any loose nails on the ground?			
Have all scaffold materials been stacked in racks?			
Are there any tripping hazards in the work area?			
Are there any unused tools in the area?			
Are there any fumes or odors in the area?			
Are there any overhead hazards in the work area?			
Is there an eyewash station in the immediate area?			
Does everyone know where the muster/rally point is?			
Are the workers wearing the proper PPE?			
Have you noticed any unsafe work acts?			

EMPLOYEE HOUSEKEEPING DAILY AUDIT

Job #:	Month Ending:
Job Name:	Location:
Audit By:	Superintendent:

General requirements: This daily audit form is to be used as a tool alongside our JSA to enhance awareness of potential job site hazards and encourage every employee to have the confidence, courage, and ability to perform basic audits.

These audits will be performed two (2) times daily. They will be maintained and, upon request, made available for inspection.

	YES	NO	Corrective Action Taken
Trash—all trash—removed from work area *(Insure trash is segregated by type; hazardous vs. non-hazardous)*			
Is there unused or old barricade tape in the area?			
Are there any loose nails on the ground?			
Have all scaffold materials been stacked in racks?			
Are there any tripping hazards in the work area?			
Are there any unused tools in the area?			
Are there any fumes or odors in the area?			
Are there any overhead hazards in the work area?			
Is there an eyewash station in the immediate area?			
Does everyone know where the muster/rally point is?			
Are the workers wearing the proper PPE?			
Have you noticed any unsafe work acts?			

EMPLOYEE HOUSEKEEPING DAILY AUDIT

Job #:	Month Ending:
Job Name:	Location:
Audit By:	Superintendent:

General requirements: This daily audit form is to be used as a tool alongside our JSA to enhance awareness of potential job site hazards and encourage every employee to have the confidence, courage, and ability to perform basic audits.

These audits will be performed two (2) times daily. They will be maintained and, upon request, made available for inspection.

	YES	NO	Corrective Action Taken
Trash—all trash—removed from work area *(Insure trash is segregated by type; hazardous vs. non-hazardous)*			
Is there unused or old barricade tape in the area?			
Are there any loose nails on the ground?			
Have all scaffold materials been stacked in racks?			
Are there any tripping hazards in the work area?			
Are there any unused tools in the area?			
Are there any fumes or odors in the area?			
Are there any overhead hazards in the work area?			
Is there an eyewash station in the immediate area?			
Does everyone know where the muster/rally point is?			
Are the workers wearing the proper PPE?			
Have you noticed any unsafe work acts?			

EMPLOYEE HOUSEKEEPING DAILY AUDIT

Job #:	Month Ending:
Job Name:	Location:
Audit By:	Superintendent:

General requirements: This daily audit form is to be used as a tool alongside our JSA to enhance awareness of potential job site hazards and encourage every employee to have the confidence, courage, and ability to perform basic audits.

These audits will be performed two (2) times daily. They will be maintained and, upon request, made available for inspection.

	YES	NO	Corrective Action Taken
Trash—all trash—removed from work area *(Insure trash is segregated by type; hazardous vs. non-hazardous)*			
Is there unused or old barricade tape in the area?			
Are there any loose nails on the ground?			
Have all scaffold materials been stacked in racks?			
Are there any tripping hazards in the work area?			
Are there any unused tools in the area?			
Are there any fumes or odors in the area?			
Are there any overhead hazards in the work area?			
Is there an eyewash station in the immediate area?			
Does everyone know where the muster/rally point is?			
Are the workers wearing the proper PPE?			
Have you noticed any unsafe work acts?			

EMPLOYEE HOUSEKEEPING DAILY AUDIT

Job #:	Month Ending:
Job Name:	Location:
Audit By:	Superintendent:

General requirements: This daily audit form is to be used as a tool alongside our JSA to enhance awareness of potential job site hazards and encourage every employee to have the confidence, courage, and ability to perform basic audits.

These audits will be performed two (2) times daily. They will be maintained and, upon request, made available for inspection.

	YES	NO	Corrective Action Taken
Trash—all trash—removed from work area *(Insure trash is segregated by type; hazardous vs. non-hazardous)*			
Is there unused or old barricade tape in the area?			
Are there any loose nails on the ground?			
Have all scaffold materials been stacked in racks?			
Are there any tripping hazards in the work area?			
Are there any unused tools in the area?			
Are there any fumes or odors in the area?			
Are there any overhead hazards in the work area?			
Is there an eyewash station in the immediate area?			
Does everyone know where the muster/rally point is?			
Are the workers wearing the proper PPE?			
Have you noticed any unsafe work acts?			

EMPLOYEE HOUSEKEEPING DAILY AUDIT

Job #:	Month Ending:
Job Name:	Location:
Audit By:	Superintendent:

General requirements: This daily audit form is to be used as a tool alongside our JSA to enhance awareness of potential job site hazards and encourage every employee to have the confidence, courage, and ability to perform basic audits.

These audits will be performed two (2) times daily. They will be maintained and, upon request, made available for inspection.

	YES	NO	Corrective Action Taken
Trash—all trash—removed from work area *(Insure trash is segregated by type; hazardous vs. non-hazardous)*			
Is there unused or old barricade tape in the area?			
Are there any loose nails on the ground?			
Have all scaffold materials been stacked in racks?			
Are there any tripping hazards in the work area?			
Are there any unused tools in the area?			
Are there any fumes or odors in the area?			
Are there any overhead hazards in the work area?			
Is there an eyewash station in the immediate area?			
Does everyone know where the muster/rally point is?			
Are the workers wearing the proper PPE?			
Have you noticed any unsafe work acts?			

EMPLOYEE HOUSEKEEPING DAILY AUDIT

Job #:	Month Ending:
Job Name:	Location:
Audit By:	Superintendent:

General requirements: This daily audit form is to be used as a tool alongside our JSA to enhance awareness of potential job site hazards and encourage every employee to have the confidence, courage, and ability to perform basic audits.

These audits will be performed two (2) times daily. They will be maintained and, upon request, made available for inspection.

	YES	NO	Corrective Action Taken
Trash—all trash—removed from work area *(Insure trash is segregated by type; hazardous vs. non-hazardous)*			
Is there unused or old barricade tape in the area?			
Are there any loose nails on the ground?			
Have all scaffold materials been stacked in racks?			
Are there any tripping hazards in the work area?			
Are there any unused tools in the area?			
Are there any fumes or odors in the area?			
Are there any overhead hazards in the work area?			
Is there an eyewash station in the immediate area?			
Does everyone know where the muster/rally point is?			
Are the workers wearing the proper PPE?			
Have you noticed any unsafe work acts?			

EMPLOYEE HOUSEKEEPING DAILY AUDIT

Job #:	Month Ending:
Job Name:	Location:
Audit By:	Superintendent:

General requirements: This daily audit form is to be used as a tool alongside our JSA to enhance awareness of potential job site hazards and encourage every employee to have the confidence, courage, and ability to perform basic audits.

These audits will be performed two (2) times daily. They will be maintained and, upon request, made available for inspection.

	YES	NO	Corrective Action Taken
Trash—all trash—removed from work area *(Insure trash is segregated by type; hazardous vs. non-hazardous)*			
Is there unused or old barricade tape in the area?			
Are there any loose nails on the ground?			
Have all scaffold materials been stacked in racks?			
Are there any tripping hazards in the work area?			
Are there any unused tools in the area?			
Are there any fumes or odors in the area?			
Are there any overhead hazards in the work area?			
Is there an eyewash station in the immediate area?			
Does everyone know where the muster/rally point is?			
Are the workers wearing the proper PPE?			
Have you noticed any unsafe work acts?			

EMPLOYEE HOUSEKEEPING DAILY AUDIT

Job #:	Month Ending:
Job Name:	Location:
Audit By:	Superintendent:

General requirements: This daily audit form is to be used as a tool alongside our JSA to enhance awareness of potential job site hazards and encourage every employee to have the confidence, courage, and ability to perform basic audits.

These audits will be performed two (2) times daily. They will be maintained and, upon request, made available for inspection.

	YES	NO	Corrective Action Taken
Trash—all trash—removed from work area *(Insure trash is segregated by type; hazardous vs. non-hazardous)*			
Is there unused or old barricade tape in the area?			
Are there any loose nails on the ground?			
Have all scaffold materials been stacked in racks?			
Are there any tripping hazards in the work area?			
Are there any unused tools in the area?			
Are there any fumes or odors in the area?			
Are there any overhead hazards in the work area?			
Is there an eyewash station in the immediate area?			
Does everyone know where the muster/rally point is?			
Are the workers wearing the proper PPE?			
Have you noticed any unsafe work acts?			

EMPLOYEE HOUSEKEEPING DAILY AUDIT

Job #:	Month Ending:
Job Name:	Location:
Audit By:	Superintendent:

General requirements: This daily audit form is to be used as a tool alongside our JSA to enhance awareness of potential job site hazards and encourage every employee to have the confidence, courage, and ability to perform basic audits.

These audits will be performed two (2) times daily. They will be maintained and, upon request, made available for inspection.

	YES	NO	Corrective Action Taken
Trash—all trash—removed from work area *(Insure trash is segregated by type; hazardous vs. non-hazardous)*			
Is there unused or old barricade tape in the area?			
Are there any loose nails on the ground?			
Have all scaffold materials been stacked in racks?			
Are there any tripping hazards in the work area?			
Are there any unused tools in the area?			
Are there any fumes or odors in the area?			
Are there any overhead hazards in the work area?			
Is there an eyewash station in the immediate area?			
Does everyone know where the muster/rally point is?			
Are the workers wearing the proper PPE?			
Have you noticed any unsafe work acts?			

EMPLOYEE HOUSEKEEPING DAILY AUDIT

Job #:	Month Ending:
Job Name:	Location:
Audit By:	Superintendent:

General requirements: This daily audit form is to be used as a tool alongside our JSA to enhance awareness of potential job site hazards and encourage every employee to have the confidence, courage, and ability to perform basic audits.

These audits will be performed two (2) times daily. They will be maintained and, upon request, made available for inspection.

	YES	NO	Corrective Action Taken
Trash—all trash—removed from work area *(Insure trash is segregated by type; hazardous vs. non-hazardous)*			
Is there unused or old barricade tape in the area?			
Are there any loose nails on the ground?			
Have all scaffold materials been stacked in racks?			
Are there any tripping hazards in the work area?			
Are there any unused tools in the area?			
Are there any fumes or odors in the area?			
Are there any overhead hazards in the work area?			
Is there an eyewash station in the immediate area?			
Does everyone know where the muster/rally point is?			
Are the workers wearing the proper PPE?			
Have you noticed any unsafe work acts?			

EMPLOYEE HOUSEKEEPING DAILY AUDIT

Job #:	Month Ending:
Job Name:	Location:
Audit By:	Superintendent:

General requirements: This daily audit form is to be used as a tool alongside our JSA to enhance awareness of potential job site hazards and encourage every employee to have the confidence, courage, and ability to perform basic audits.

These audits will be performed two (2) times daily. They will be maintained and, upon request, made available for inspection.

	YES	NO	Corrective Action Taken
Trash—all trash—removed from work area *(Insure trash is segregated by type; hazardous vs. non-hazardous)*			
Is there unused or old barricade tape in the area?			
Are there any loose nails on the ground?			
Have all scaffold materials been stacked in racks?			
Are there any tripping hazards in the work area?			
Are there any unused tools in the area?			
Are there any fumes or odors in the area?			
Are there any overhead hazards in the work area?			
Is there an eyewash station in the immediate area?			
Does everyone know where the muster/rally point is?			
Are the workers wearing the proper PPE?			
Have you noticed any unsafe work acts?			

EMPLOYEE HOUSEKEEPING DAILY AUDIT

Job #:	Month Ending:
Job Name:	Location:
Audit By:	Superintendent:

General requirements: This daily audit form is to be used as a tool alongside our JSA to enhance awareness of potential job site hazards and encourage every employee to have the confidence, courage, and ability to perform basic audits.

These audits will be performed two (2) times daily. They will be maintained and, upon request, made available for inspection.

	YES	NO	Corrective Action Taken
Trash—all trash—removed from work area *(Insure trash is segregated by type; hazardous vs. non-hazardous)*			
Is there unused or old barricade tape in the area?			
Are there any loose nails on the ground?			
Have all scaffold materials been stacked in racks?			
Are there any tripping hazards in the work area?			
Are there any unused tools in the area?			
Are there any fumes or odors in the area?			
Are there any overhead hazards in the work area?			
Is there an eyewash station in the immediate area?			
Does everyone know where the muster/rally point is?			
Are the workers wearing the proper PPE?			
Have you noticed any unsafe work acts?			

EMPLOYEE HOUSEKEEPING DAILY AUDIT

Job #:	Month Ending:
Job Name:	Location:
Audit By:	Superintendent:

General requirements: This daily audit form is to be used as a tool alongside our JSA to enhance awareness of potential job site hazards and encourage every employee to have the confidence, courage, and ability to perform basic audits.

These audits will be performed two (2) times daily. They will be maintained and, upon request, made available for inspection.

	YES	NO	Corrective Action Taken
Trash—all trash—removed from work area *(Insure trash is segregated by type; hazardous vs. non-hazardous)*			
Is there unused or old barricade tape in the area?			
Are there any loose nails on the ground?			
Have all scaffold materials been stacked in racks?			
Are there any tripping hazards in the work area?			
Are there any unused tools in the area?			
Are there any fumes or odors in the area?			
Are there any overhead hazards in the work area?			
Is there an eyewash station in the immediate area?			
Does everyone know where the muster/rally point is?			
Are the workers wearing the proper PPE?			
Have you noticed any unsafe work acts?			

EMPLOYEE HOUSEKEEPING DAILY AUDIT

Job #:	Month Ending:
Job Name:	Location:
Audit By:	Superintendent:

General requirements: This daily audit form is to be used as a tool alongside our JSA to enhance awareness of potential job site hazards and encourage every employee to have the confidence, courage, and ability to perform basic audits.

These audits will be performed two (2) times daily. They will be maintained and, upon request, made available for inspection.

	YES	NO	Corrective Action Taken
Trash—all trash—removed from work area *(Insure trash is segregated by type; hazardous vs. non-hazardous)*			
Is there unused or old barricade tape in the area?			
Are there any loose nails on the ground?			
Have all scaffold materials been stacked in racks?			
Are there any tripping hazards in the work area?			
Are there any unused tools in the area?			
Are there any fumes or odors in the area?			
Are there any overhead hazards in the work area?			
Is there an eyewash station in the immediate area?			
Does everyone know where the muster/rally point is?			
Are the workers wearing the proper PPE?			
Have you noticed any unsafe work acts?			

PROJECT EVALUATION
FORM

PROJECT EVALUATION

Date:	Project Name:		Job #:
Contract:		☐ Lump Sum	☐ Cost Plus
Project Location:			
Superintendent:			

SAFETY		
FIRST AID LOG	☐ Yes	☐ No
OSHA 200 LOG	☐ Posted	☐ Not Posted
RIGHT-TO-KNOW LAW POSTERS	☐ Posted	☐ Not Posted
EVACUATION PROCEDURES	☐ Posted	☐ Not Posted
FIRST AID KIT COMPLETE	☐ Yes	☐ No
HARNESS INSPECTION LOG	☐ Yes	☐ No
SAFETY MEETING LOG	☐ Yes	☐ No
EMPLOYEE FILE STATUS	☐ Yes	☐ No
SIGN IN/OUT LOG	☐ Yes	☐ No
IS PROJECT ON SCHEDULE?	☐ Yes	☐ No
HOUSEKEEPING	☐ Good	☐ Needs Improvement

COMMENTS

Printed Name:	
Signature:	

PROJECT EVALUATION

Date:	Project Name:		Job #:
Contract:		☐ Lump Sum	☐ Cost Plus
Project Location:			
Superintendent:			

SAFETY		
FIRST AID LOG	☐ Yes	☐ No
OSHA 200 LOG	☐ Posted	☐ Not Posted
RIGHT-TO-KNOW LAW POSTERS	☐ Posted	☐ Not Posted
EVACUATION PROCEDURES	☐ Posted	☐ Not Posted
FIRST AID KIT COMPLETE	☐ Yes	☐ No
HARNESS INSPECTION LOG	☐ Yes	☐ No
SAFETY MEETING LOG	☐ Yes	☐ No
EMPLOYEE FILE STATUS	☐ Yes	☐ No
SIGN IN/OUT LOG	☐ Yes	☐ No
IS PROJECT ON SCHEDULE?	☐ Yes	☐ No
HOUSEKEEPING	☐ Good	☐ Needs Improvement

COMMENTS

Printed Name:	
Signature:	

PROJECT EVALUATION

Date:	Project Name:		Job #:
Contract:		☐ Lump Sum	☐ Cost Plus
Project Location:			
Superintendent:			

SAFETY		
FIRST AID LOG	☐ Yes	☐ No
OSHA 200 LOG	☐ Posted	☐ Not Posted
RIGHT-TO-KNOW LAW POSTERS	☐ Posted	☐ Not Posted
EVACUATION PROCEDURES	☐ Posted	☐ Not Posted
FIRST AID KIT COMPLETE	☐ Yes	☐ No
HARNESS INSPECTION LOG	☐ Yes	☐ No
SAFETY MEETING LOG	☐ Yes	☐ No
EMPLOYEE FILE STATUS	☐ Yes	☐ No
SIGN IN/OUT LOG	☐ Yes	☐ No
IS PROJECT ON SCHEDULE?	☐ Yes	☐ No
HOUSEKEEPING	☐ Good	☐ Needs Improvement

COMMENTS

Printed Name:	
Signature:	

PROJECT EVALUATION

Date:	Project Name:		Job #:	
Contract:		☐ Lump Sum	☐ Cost Plus	
Project Location:				
Superintendent:				
SAFETY				
FIRST AID LOG		☐ Yes	☐ No	
OSHA 200 LOG		☐ Posted	☐ Not Posted	
RIGHT-TO-KNOW LAW POSTERS		☐ Posted	☐ Not Posted	
EVACUATION PROCEDURES		☐ Posted	☐ Not Posted	
FIRST AID KIT COMPLETE		☐ Yes	☐ No	
HARNESS INSPECTION LOG		☐ Yes	☐ No	
SAFETY MEETING LOG		☐ Yes	☐ No	
EMPLOYEE FILE STATUS		☐ Yes	☐ No	
SIGN IN/OUT LOG		☐ Yes	☐ No	
IS PROJECT ON SCHEDULE?		☐ Yes	☐ No	
HOUSEKEEPING		☐ Good	☐ Needs Improvement	
COMMENTS				

Printed Name:	
Signature:	

PROJECT EVALUATION

Date:	Project Name:		Job #:
Contract:		☐ Lump Sum	☐ Cost Plus
Project Location:			
Superintendent:			

SAFETY		
FIRST AID LOG	☐ Yes	☐ No
OSHA 200 LOG	☐ Posted	☐ Not Posted
RIGHT-TO-KNOW LAW POSTERS	☐ Posted	☐ Not Posted
EVACUATION PROCEDURES	☐ Posted	☐ Not Posted
FIRST AID KIT COMPLETE	☐ Yes	☐ No
HARNESS INSPECTION LOG	☐ Yes	☐ No
SAFETY MEETING LOG	☐ Yes	☐ No
EMPLOYEE FILE STATUS	☐ Yes	☐ No
SIGN IN/OUT LOG	☐ Yes	☐ No
IS PROJECT ON SCHEDULE?	☐ Yes	☐ No
HOUSEKEEPING	☐ Good	☐ Needs Improvement

COMMENTS

Printed Name:	
Signature:	

PROJECT EVALUATION

Date:	Project Name:		Job #:
Contract:		☐ Lump Sum	☐ Cost Plus
Project Location:			
Superintendent:			
SAFETY			
FIRST AID LOG	☐ Yes		☐ No
OSHA 200 LOG	☐ Posted		☐ Not Posted
RIGHT-TO-KNOW LAW POSTERS	☐ Posted		☐ Not Posted
EVACUATION PROCEDURES	☐ Posted		☐ Not Posted
FIRST AID KIT COMPLETE	☐ Yes		☐ No
HARNESS INSPECTION LOG	☐ Yes		☐ No
SAFETY MEETING LOG	☐ Yes		☐ No
EMPLOYEE FILE STATUS	☐ Yes		☐ No
SIGN IN/OUT LOG	☐ Yes		☐ No
IS PROJECT ON SCHEDULE?	☐ Yes		☐ No
HOUSEKEEPING	☐ Good		☐ Needs Improvement
COMMENTS			
Printed Name:			
Signature:			

PROJECT EVALUATION

Date:	Project Name:		Job #:
Contract:		☐ Lump Sum	☐ Cost Plus
Project Location:			
Superintendent:			

SAFETY		
FIRST AID LOG	☐ Yes	☐ No
OSHA 200 LOG	☐ Posted	☐ Not Posted
RIGHT-TO-KNOW LAW POSTERS	☐ Posted	☐ Not Posted
EVACUATION PROCEDURES	☐ Posted	☐ Not Posted
FIRST AID KIT COMPLETE	☐ Yes	☐ No
HARNESS INSPECTION LOG	☐ Yes	☐ No
SAFETY MEETING LOG	☐ Yes	☐ No
EMPLOYEE FILE STATUS	☐ Yes	☐ No
SIGN IN/OUT LOG	☐ Yes	☐ No
IS PROJECT ON SCHEDULE?	☐ Yes	☐ No
HOUSEKEEPING	☐ Good	☐ Needs Improvement

COMMENTS

Printed Name:	
Signature:	

PROJECT EVALUATION

Date:	Project Name:		Job #:	
Contract:		☐ Lump Sum	☐ Cost Plus	
Project Location:				
Superintendent:				
SAFETY				
FIRST AID LOG	☐ Yes		☐ No	
OSHA 200 LOG	☐ Posted		☐ Not Posted	
RIGHT-TO-KNOW LAW POSTERS	☐ Posted		☐ Not Posted	
EVACUATION PROCEDURES	☐ Posted		☐ Not Posted	
FIRST AID KIT COMPLETE	☐ Yes		☐ No	
HARNESS INSPECTION LOG	☐ Yes		☐ No	
SAFETY MEETING LOG	☐ Yes		☐ No	
EMPLOYEE FILE STATUS	☐ Yes		☐ No	
SIGN IN/OUT LOG	☐ Yes		☐ No	
IS PROJECT ON SCHEDULE?	☐ Yes		☐ No	
HOUSEKEEPING	☐ Good		☐ Needs Improvement	
COMMENTS				
Printed Name:				
Signature:				

PROJECT EVALUATION

Date:	Project Name:		Job #:
Contract:		☐ Lump Sum	☐ Cost Plus
Project Location:			
Superintendent:			

SAFETY		
FIRST AID LOG	☐ Yes	☐ No
OSHA 200 LOG	☐ Posted	☐ Not Posted
RIGHT-TO-KNOW LAW POSTERS	☐ Posted	☐ Not Posted
EVACUATION PROCEDURES	☐ Posted	☐ Not Posted
FIRST AID KIT COMPLETE	☐ Yes	☐ No
HARNESS INSPECTION LOG	☐ Yes	☐ No
SAFETY MEETING LOG	☐ Yes	☐ No
EMPLOYEE FILE STATUS	☐ Yes	☐ No
SIGN IN/OUT LOG	☐ Yes	☐ No
IS PROJECT ON SCHEDULE?	☐ Yes	☐ No
HOUSEKEEPING	☐ Good	☐ Needs Improvement

COMMENTS

Printed Name:	
Signature:	

PROJECT EVALUATION

Date:	Project Name:		Job #:
Contract:		☐ Lump Sum	☐ Cost Plus
Project Location:			
Superintendent:			
SAFETY			
FIRST AID LOG		☐ Yes	☐ No
OSHA 200 LOG		☐ Posted	☐ Not Posted
RIGHT-TO-KNOW LAW POSTERS		☐ Posted	☐ Not Posted
EVACUATION PROCEDURES		☐ Posted	☐ Not Posted
FIRST AID KIT COMPLETE		☐ Yes	☐ No
HARNESS INSPECTION LOG		☐ Yes	☐ No
SAFETY MEETING LOG		☐ Yes	☐ No
EMPLOYEE FILE STATUS		☐ Yes	☐ No
SIGN IN/OUT LOG		☐ Yes	☐ No
IS PROJECT ON SCHEDULE?		☐ Yes	☐ No
HOUSEKEEPING		☐ Good	☐ Needs Improvement
COMMENTS			

Printed Name:	
Signature:	

PROJECT EVALUATION

Date:	Project Name:		Job #:
Contract:		☐ Lump Sum	☐ Cost Plus
Project Location:			
Superintendent:			

SAFETY		
FIRST AID LOG	☐ Yes	☐ No
OSHA 200 LOG	☐ Posted	☐ Not Posted
RIGHT-TO-KNOW LAW POSTERS	☐ Posted	☐ Not Posted
EVACUATION PROCEDURES	☐ Posted	☐ Not Posted
FIRST AID KIT COMPLETE	☐ Yes	☐ No
HARNESS INSPECTION LOG	☐ Yes	☐ No
SAFETY MEETING LOG	☐ Yes	☐ No
EMPLOYEE FILE STATUS	☐ Yes	☐ No
SIGN IN/OUT LOG	☐ Yes	☐ No
IS PROJECT ON SCHEDULE?	☐ Yes	☐ No
HOUSEKEEPING	☐ Good	☐ Needs Improvement

COMMENTS

Printed Name:	
Signature:	

PROJECT EVALUATION

Date:	Project Name:		Job #:	
Contract:		☐ Lump Sum	☐ Cost Plus	
Project Location:				
Superintendent:				

SAFETY		
FIRST AID LOG	☐ Yes	☐ No
OSHA 200 LOG	☐ Posted	☐ Not Posted
RIGHT-TO-KNOW LAW POSTERS	☐ Posted	☐ Not Posted
EVACUATION PROCEDURES	☐ Posted	☐ Not Posted
FIRST AID KIT COMPLETE	☐ Yes	☐ No
HARNESS INSPECTION LOG	☐ Yes	☐ No
SAFETY MEETING LOG	☐ Yes	☐ No
EMPLOYEE FILE STATUS	☐ Yes	☐ No
SIGN IN/OUT LOG	☐ Yes	☐ No
IS PROJECT ON SCHEDULE?	☐ Yes	☐ No
HOUSEKEEPING	☐ Good	☐ Needs Improvement

COMMENTS

Printed Name:	
Signature:	

PROJECT EVALUATION

Date:	Project Name:		Job #:
Contract:		☐ Lump Sum	☐ Cost Plus
Project Location:			
Superintendent:			

SAFETY		
FIRST AID LOG	☐ Yes	☐ No
OSHA 200 LOG	☐ Posted	☐ Not Posted
RIGHT-TO-KNOW LAW POSTERS	☐ Posted	☐ Not Posted
EVACUATION PROCEDURES	☐ Posted	☐ Not Posted
FIRST AID KIT COMPLETE	☐ Yes	☐ No
HARNESS INSPECTION LOG	☐ Yes	☐ No
SAFETY MEETING LOG	☐ Yes	☐ No
EMPLOYEE FILE STATUS	☐ Yes	☐ No
SIGN IN/OUT LOG	☐ Yes	☐ No
IS PROJECT ON SCHEDULE?	☐ Yes	☐ No
HOUSEKEEPING	☐ Good	☐ Needs Improvement

COMMENTS

Printed Name:	
Signature:	

PROJECT EVALUATION

Date:	Project Name:		Job #:	
Contract:		☐ Lump Sum	☐ Cost Plus	
Project Location:				
Superintendent:				
SAFETY				
FIRST AID LOG	☐ Yes		☐ No	
OSHA 200 LOG	☐ Posted		☐ Not Posted	
RIGHT-TO-KNOW LAW POSTERS	☐ Posted		☐ Not Posted	
EVACUATION PROCEDURES	☐ Posted		☐ Not Posted	
FIRST AID KIT COMPLETE	☐ Yes		☐ No	
HARNESS INSPECTION LOG	☐ Yes		☐ No	
SAFETY MEETING LOG	☐ Yes		☐ No	
EMPLOYEE FILE STATUS	☐ Yes		☐ No	
SIGN IN/OUT LOG	☐ Yes		☐ No	
IS PROJECT ON SCHEDULE?	☐ Yes		☐ No	
HOUSEKEEPING	☐ Good		☐ Needs Improvement	
COMMENTS				

Printed Name:	
Signature:	

PROJECT EVALUATION

Date:	Project Name:		Job #:
Contract:		☐ Lump Sum	☐ Cost Plus
Project Location:			
Superintendent:			
SAFETY			
FIRST AID LOG	☐ Yes		☐ No
OSHA 200 LOG	☐ Posted		☐ Not Posted
RIGHT-TO-KNOW LAW POSTERS	☐ Posted		☐ Not Posted
EVACUATION PROCEDURES	☐ Posted		☐ Not Posted
FIRST AID KIT COMPLETE	☐ Yes		☐ No
HARNESS INSPECTION LOG	☐ Yes		☐ No
SAFETY MEETING LOG	☐ Yes		☐ No
EMPLOYEE FILE STATUS	☐ Yes		☐ No
SIGN IN/OUT LOG	☐ Yes		☐ No
IS PROJECT ON SCHEDULE?	☐ Yes		☐ No
HOUSEKEEPING	☐ Good		☐ Needs Improvement
COMMENTS			
Printed Name:			
Signature:			

ABRASIVE SIEVE TEST
REPORT DATA

ABRASIVE SIEVE TEST REPORT DATA

TYPE OF ABRASIVE	
SUPPLIER	
JOB TITLE	
SPECIFIC LOCATION	
INITIAL WEIGHT OF SAMPLE	
OPTIONAL ABRASIVE DATA	
WAYBILL/INVOICE #	

MESH SIZE	WT. RETAINED	% WT. PASSING	%WT. RETAINED

DATE		INSPECTOR	

1. To calculate % Wt. Retained: (Wt. Retained X 100) Initial Wt. of Sample
2. To calculate % Wt. Passing: (100 minus % Wt. Retained) [this figure is cumulative]
3. It is recommended that the Initial Sample Weight is selected to give easy calculation (e.g. 100 gm, 10 lbs)

PASS OR FAIL:	

ABRASIVE SIEVE TEST REPORT DATA

TYPE OF ABRASIVE	
SUPPLIER	
JOB TITLE	
SPECIFIC LOCATION	
INITIAL WEIGHT OF SAMPLE	
OPTIONAL ABRASIVE DATA	
WAYBILL/INVOICE #	

MESH SIZE	WT. RETAINED	% WT. PASSING	%WT. RETAINED

DATE		INSPECTOR	

1. To calculate % Wt. Retained: (Wt. Retained X 100) Initial Wt. of Sample
2. To calculate % Wt. Passing: (100 minus % Wt. Retained) [this figure is cumulative]
3. It is recommended that the Initial Sample Weight is selected to give easy calculation (e.g. 100 gm, 10 lbs)

PASS OR FAIL:	

ABRASIVE SIEVE TEST REPORT DATA

TYPE OF ABRASIVE	
SUPPLIER	
JOB TITLE	
SPECIFIC LOCATION	
INITIAL WEIGHT OF SAMPLE	
OPTIONAL ABRASIVE DATA	
WAYBILL/INVOICE #	

MESH SIZE	WT. RETAINED	% WT. PASSING	%WT. RETAINED

DATE		INSPECTOR	

1. To calculate % Wt. Retained: (Wt. Retained X 100) Initial Wt. of Sample
2. To calculate % Wt. Passing: (100 minus % Wt. Retained) [this figure is cumulative]
3. It is recommended that the Initial Sample Weight is selected to give easy calculation (e.g. 100 gm, 10 lbs)

PASS OR FAIL:	

WEEKLY CONTAINMENT INTEGRITY INSPECTION AND RECORD OF WASTE MATERIALS STORED AND USED AT SITE

CONTAINMENT INTEGRITY EVALUATION

It is the responsibility of everyone to protect the environment. The containment must be maintained and thus inspected routinely. The following forms provide an area for such documentation.

WEEKLY CONTAINMENT INTEGRITY INSPECTION AND RECORD OF WASTE MATERIALS STORED AND USED AT SITE

JOB TITLE

SPECIFIC LOCATION

INSTRUCTIONS

1. Complete this form for each inspection
2. Observe and maintain entire area
3. Maintain form in file

Tank/Area	Date Inspected	Integrity of Containment Area Achieved	Source/Cause of Losses to Environment	Total Time of Containment Leakage	Quantity of Residues Removed	Notes
		☐ Yes ☐ No ☐ N/A	☐ Leak ☐ Damage ☐ Tear ☐ Block	☐ <30 min ☐ 1–2 hrs ☐ >2 hrs ☐ N/A	☐ None _____ drums ☐ N/A _____ gals	
		☐ Yes ☐ No ☐ N/A	☐ Leak ☐ Damage ☐ Tear ☐ Block	☐ <30 min ☐ 1–2 hrs ☐ >2 hrs ☐ N/A	☐ None _____ drums ☐ N/A _____ gals	
		☐ Yes ☐ No ☐ N/A	☐ Leak ☐ Damage ☐ Tear ☐ Block	☐ <30 min ☐ 1–2 hrs ☐ >2 hrs ☐ N/A	☐ None _____ drums ☐ N/A _____ gals	
		☐ Yes ☐ No ☐ N/A	☐ Leak ☐ Damage ☐ Tear ☐ Block	☐ <30 min ☐ 1–2 hrs ☐ >2 hrs ☐ N/A	☐ None _____ drums ☐ N/A _____ gals	
		☐ Yes ☐ No ☐ N/A	☐ Leak ☐ Damage ☐ Tear ☐ Block	☐ <30 min ☐ 1–2 hrs ☐ >2 hrs ☐ N/A	☐ None _____ drums ☐ N/A _____ gals	
		☐ Yes ☐ No ☐ N/A	☐ Leak ☐ Damage ☐ Tear ☐ Block	☐ <30 min ☐ 1–2 hrs ☐ >2 hrs ☐ N/A	☐ None _____ drums ☐ N/A _____ gals	
		☐ Yes ☐ No ☐ N/A	☐ Leak ☐ Damage ☐ Tear ☐ Block	☐ <30 min ☐ 1–2 hrs ☐ >2 hrs ☐ N/A	☐ None _____ drums ☐ N/A _____ gals	

CONTAINMENT SEALS

CONTAINMENT MATERIAL

VOLUME WASTE CONTAINED

CONTAINMENT ATTACHMENT

VOLUME USED

VOLUME LOST

CONTAINMENT AREA INTEGRITY REVIVIFIED

INSPECTED BY

DATE

REPORT #

ENVIRONMENTAL MANAGER REVIEW DATE

152

WEEKLY CONTAINMENT INTEGRITY INSPECTION AND RECORD OF WASTE MATERIALS STORED AND USED AT SITE

JOB TITLE

SPECIFIC LOCATION

INSTRUCTIONS

1. Complete this form for each inspection
2. Observe and maintain entire area
3. Maintain form in file

Tank/Area	Date Inspected	Integrity of Containment Area Achieved	Source/Cause of Losses to Environment	Total Time of Containment Leakage	Quantity of Residues Removed	Notes
		☐ Yes ☐ No ☐ N/A	☐ Leak ☐ Damage ☐ Tear ☐ Block	☐ <30 min ☐ 1–2 hrs ☐ >2 hrs ☐ N/A	☐ None ☐ _____ drums ☐ N/A ☐ _____ gals	
		☐ Yes ☐ No ☐ N/A	☐ Leak ☐ Damage ☐ Tear ☐ Block	☐ <30 min ☐ 1–2 hrs ☐ >2 hrs ☐ N/A	☐ None ☐ _____ drums ☐ N/A ☐ _____ gals	
		☐ Yes ☐ No ☐ N/A	☐ Leak ☐ Damage ☐ Tear ☐ Block	☐ <30 min ☐ 1–2 hrs ☐ >2 hrs ☐ N/A	☐ None ☐ _____ drums ☐ N/A ☐ _____ gals	
		☐ Yes ☐ No ☐ N/A	☐ Leak ☐ Damage ☐ Tear ☐ Block	☐ <30 min ☐ 1–2 hrs ☐ >2 hrs ☐ N/A	☐ None ☐ _____ drums ☐ N/A ☐ _____ gals	
		☐ Yes ☐ No ☐ N/A	☐ Leak ☐ Damage ☐ Tear ☐ Block	☐ <30 min ☐ 1–2 hrs ☐ >2 hrs ☐ N/A	☐ None ☐ _____ drums ☐ N/A ☐ _____ gals	
		☐ Yes ☐ No ☐ N/A	☐ Leak ☐ Damage ☐ Tear ☐ Block	☐ <30 min ☐ 1–2 hrs ☐ >2 hrs ☐ N/A	☐ None ☐ _____ drums ☐ N/A ☐ _____ gals	
		☐ Yes ☐ No ☐ N/A	☐ Leak ☐ Damage ☐ Tear ☐ Block	☐ <30 min ☐ 1–2 hrs ☐ >2 hrs ☐ N/A	☐ None ☐ _____ drums ☐ N/A ☐ _____ gals	

CONTAINMENT SEALS

CONTAINMENT MATERIAL

VOLUME WASTE CONTAINED

CONTAINMENT ATTACHMENT

VOLUME USED

VOLUME LOST

CONTAINMENT AREA INTEGRITY REVIVIFIED

DATE | **INSPECTED BY**

REPORT #

ENVIRONMENTAL MANAGER REVIEW DATE

WEEKLY CONTAINMENT INTEGRITY INSPECTION AND RECORD OF WASTE MATERIALS STORED AND USED AT SITE

JOB TITLE | **SPECIFIC LOCATION**

INSTRUCTIONS

1. Complete this form for each inspection
2. Observe and maintain entire area
3. Maintain form in file

Tank/Area	Date Inspected	Integrity of Containment Area Achieved	Source/Cause of Losses to Environment	Total Time of Containment Leakage	Quantity of Residues Removed	Notes
		☐ Yes ☐ No ☐ N/A	☐ Leak ☐ Damage ☐ Tear ☐ Block	☐ <30 min ☐ 1–2 hrs ☐ >2 hrs ☐ N/A	☐ None _____ drums ☐ N/A _____ gals	
		☐ Yes ☐ No ☐ N/A	☐ Leak ☐ Damage ☐ Tear ☐ Block	☐ <30 min ☐ 1–2 hrs ☐ >2 hrs ☐ N/A	☐ None _____ drums ☐ N/A _____ gals	
		☐ Yes ☐ No ☐ N/A	☐ Leak ☐ Damage ☐ Tear ☐ Block	☐ <30 min ☐ 1–2 hrs ☐ >2 hrs ☐ N/A	☐ None _____ drums ☐ N/A _____ gals	
		☐ Yes ☐ No ☐ N/A	☐ Leak ☐ Damage ☐ Tear ☐ Block	☐ <30 min ☐ 1–2 hrs ☐ >2 hrs ☐ N/A	☐ None _____ drums ☐ N/A _____ gals	
		☐ Yes ☐ No ☐ N/A	☐ Leak ☐ Damage ☐ Tear ☐ Block	☐ <30 min ☐ 1–2 hrs ☐ >2 hrs ☐ N/A	☐ None _____ drums ☐ N/A _____ gals	
		☐ Yes ☐ No ☐ N/A	☐ Leak ☐ Damage ☐ Tear ☐ Block	☐ <30 min ☐ 1–2 hrs ☐ >2 hrs ☐ N/A	☐ None _____ drums ☐ N/A _____ gals	
		☐ Yes ☐ No ☐ N/A	☐ Leak ☐ Damage ☐ Tear ☐ Block	☐ <30 min ☐ 1–2 hrs ☐ >2 hrs ☐ N/A	☐ None _____ drums ☐ N/A _____ gals	

CONTAINMENT SEALS		CONTAINMENT ATTACHMENT
CONTAINMENT MATERIAL		VOLUME USED
VOLUME WASTE CONTAINED		VOLUME LOST
INSPECTED BY	CONTAINMENT AREA INTEGRITY REVIVIFIED	
DATE	REPORT #	ENVIRONMENTAL MANAGER REVIEW DATE

WEEKLY CONTAINMENT INTEGRITY INSPECTION AND RECORD OF WASTE MATERIALS STORED AND USED AT SITE

JOB TITLE _____   SPECIFIC LOCATION _____

INSTRUCTIONS

1. Complete this form for each inspection
2. Observe and maintain entire area
3. Maintain form in file

Tank/Area	Date Inspected	Integrity of Containment Area Achieved	Source/Cause of Losses to Environment	Total Time of Containment Leakage	Quantity of Residues Removed	Notes
		☐ Yes ☐ No ☐ N/A	☐ Leak ☐ Damage ☐ Tear ☐ Block	☐ <30 min ☐ 1–2 hrs ☐ >2 hrs ☐ N/A	☐ None ☐ N/A ☐ _____ drums ☐ _____ gals	
		☐ Yes ☐ No ☐ N/A	☐ Leak ☐ Damage ☐ Tear ☐ Block	☐ <30 min ☐ 1–2 hrs ☐ >2 hrs ☐ N/A	☐ None ☐ N/A ☐ _____ drums ☐ _____ gals	
		☐ Yes ☐ No ☐ N/A	☐ Leak ☐ Damage ☐ Tear ☐ Block	☐ <30 min ☐ 1–2 hrs ☐ >2 hrs ☐ N/A	☐ None ☐ N/A ☐ _____ drums ☐ _____ gals	
		☐ Yes ☐ No ☐ N/A	☐ Leak ☐ Damage ☐ Tear ☐ Block	☐ <30 min ☐ 1–2 hrs ☐ >2 hrs ☐ N/A	☐ None ☐ N/A ☐ _____ drums ☐ _____ gals	
		☐ Yes ☐ No ☐ N/A	☐ Leak ☐ Damage ☐ Tear ☐ Block	☐ <30 min ☐ 1–2 hrs ☐ >2 hrs ☐ N/A	☐ None ☐ N/A ☐ _____ drums ☐ _____ gals	
		☐ Yes ☐ No ☐ N/A	☐ Leak ☐ Damage ☐ Tear ☐ Block	☐ <30 min ☐ 1–2 hrs ☐ >2 hrs ☐ N/A	☐ None ☐ N/A ☐ _____ drums ☐ _____ gals	
		☐ Yes ☐ No ☐ N/A	☐ Leak ☐ Damage ☐ Tear ☐ Block	☐ <30 min ☐ 1–2 hrs ☐ >2 hrs ☐ N/A	☐ None ☐ N/A ☐ _____ drums ☐ _____ gals	

CONTAINMENT SEALS		CONTAINMENT ATTACHMENT	
CONTAINMENT MATERIAL		VOLUME USED	
VOLUME WASTE CONTAINED		VOLUME LOST	
INSPECTED BY		CONTAINMENT AREA INTEGRITY REVIVIFIED	
DATE		ENVIRONMENTAL MANAGER REVIEW DATE	
REPORT #			

WEEKLY CONTAINMENT INTEGRITY INSPECTION AND RECORD OF WASTE MATERIALS STORED AND USED AT SITE

JOB TITLE

SPECIFIC LOCATION

INSTRUCTIONS

1. Complete this form for each inspection
2. Observe and maintain entire area
3. Maintain form in file

Tank/Area	Date Inspected	Integrity of Containment Area Achieved	Source/Cause of Losses to Environment	Total Time of Containment Leakage	Quantity of Residues Removed	Notes
		☐ Yes ☐ No ☐ N/A	☐ Leak ☐ Damage ☐ Tear ☐ Block	☐ <30 min ☐ 1–2 hrs ☐ >2 hrs ☐ N/A	☐ None ☐ ___ drums ☐ N/A ☐ ___ gals	
		☐ Yes ☐ No ☐ N/A	☐ Leak ☐ Damage ☐ Tear ☐ Block	☐ <30 min ☐ 1–2 hrs ☐ >2 hrs ☐ N/A	☐ None ☐ ___ drums ☐ N/A ☐ ___ gals	
		☐ Yes ☐ No ☐ N/A	☐ Leak ☐ Damage ☐ Tear ☐ Block	☐ <30 min ☐ 1–2 hrs ☐ >2 hrs ☐ N/A	☐ None ☐ ___ drums ☐ N/A ☐ ___ gals	
		☐ Yes ☐ No ☐ N/A	☐ Leak ☐ Damage ☐ Tear ☐ Block	☐ <30 min ☐ 1–2 hrs ☐ >2 hrs ☐ N/A	☐ None ☐ ___ drums ☐ N/A ☐ ___ gals	
		☐ Yes ☐ No ☐ N/A	☐ Leak ☐ Damage ☐ Tear ☐ Block	☐ <30 min ☐ 1–2 hrs ☐ >2 hrs ☐ N/A	☐ None ☐ ___ drums ☐ N/A ☐ ___ gals	
		☐ Yes ☐ No ☐ N/A	☐ Leak ☐ Damage ☐ Tear ☐ Block	☐ <30 min ☐ 1–2 hrs ☐ >2 hrs ☐ N/A	☐ None ☐ ___ drums ☐ N/A ☐ ___ gals	
		☐ Yes ☐ No ☐ N/A	☐ Leak ☐ Damage ☐ Tear ☐ Block	☐ <30 min ☐ 1–2 hrs ☐ >2 hrs ☐ N/A	☐ None ☐ ___ drums ☐ N/A ☐ ___ gals	

CONTAINMENT SEALS

CONTAINMENT MATERIAL

VOLUME WASTE CONTAINED

CONTAINMENT AREA INTEGRITY REVIVIFIED

CONTAINMENT ATTACHMENT

VOLUME USED

VOLUME LOST

DATE

INSPECTED BY

REPORT #

ENVIRONMENTAL MANAGER REVIEW DATE

WEEKLY CONTAINMENT INTEGRITY INSPECTION AND RECORD OF WASTE MATERIALS STORED AND USED AT SITE

JOB TITLE _____   SPECIFIC LOCATION _____

INSTRUCTIONS
1. Complete this form for each inspection
2. Observe and maintain entire area
3. Maintain form in file

Tank/Area	Date Inspected	Integrity of Containment Area Achieved	Source/Cause of Losses to Environment	Total Time of Containment Leakage	Quantity of Residues Removed	Notes
		☐ Yes ☐ No ☐ N/A	☐ Leak ☐ Damage ☐ Tear ☐ Block	☐ <30 min ☐ 1-2 hrs ☐ >2 hrs ☐ N/A	☐ None ☐ _____ drums ☐ N/A ☐ _____ gals	
		☐ Yes ☐ No ☐ N/A	☐ Leak ☐ Damage ☐ Tear ☐ Block	☐ <30 min ☐ 1-2 hrs ☐ >2 hrs ☐ N/A	☐ None ☐ _____ drums ☐ N/A ☐ _____ gals	
		☐ Yes ☐ No ☐ N/A	☐ Leak ☐ Damage ☐ Tear ☐ Block	☐ <30 min ☐ 1-2 hrs ☐ >2 hrs ☐ N/A	☐ None ☐ _____ drums ☐ N/A ☐ _____ gals	
		☐ Yes ☐ No ☐ N/A	☐ Leak ☐ Damage ☐ Tear ☐ Block	☐ <30 min ☐ 1-2 hrs ☐ >2 hrs ☐ N/A	☐ None ☐ _____ drums ☐ N/A ☐ _____ gals	
		☐ Yes ☐ No ☐ N/A	☐ Leak ☐ Damage ☐ Tear ☐ Block	☐ <30 min ☐ 1-2 hrs ☐ >2 hrs ☐ N/A	☐ None ☐ _____ drums ☐ N/A ☐ _____ gals	
		☐ Yes ☐ No ☐ N/A	☐ Leak ☐ Damage ☐ Tear ☐ Block	☐ <30 min ☐ 1-2 hrs ☐ >2 hrs ☐ N/A	☐ None ☐ _____ drums ☐ N/A ☐ _____ gals	
		☐ Yes ☐ No ☐ N/A	☐ Leak ☐ Damage ☐ Tear ☐ Block	☐ <30 min ☐ 1-2 hrs ☐ >2 hrs ☐ N/A	☐ None ☐ _____ drums ☐ N/A ☐ _____ gals	
		☐ Yes ☐ No ☐ N/A	☐ Leak ☐ Damage ☐ Tear ☐ Block	☐ <30 min ☐ 1-2 hrs ☐ >2 hrs ☐ N/A	☐ None ☐ _____ drums ☐ N/A ☐ _____ gals	

CONTAINMENT SEALS _____   CONTAINMENT ATTACHMENT _____

CONTAINMENT MATERIAL _____   VOLUME USED _____

VOLUME WASTE CONTAINED _____   VOLUME LOST _____

CONTAINMENT AREA INTEGRITY REVIVIFIED _____

DATE _____   INSPECTED BY _____   ENVIRONMENTAL MANAGER REVIEW DATE _____

REPORT # _____

WEEKLY CONTAINMENT INTEGRITY INSPECTION AND RECORD OF WASTE MATERIALS STORED AND USED AT SITE

JOB TITLE

SPECIFIC LOCATION

INSTRUCTIONS

1. Complete this form for each inspection
2. Observe and maintain entire area
3. Maintain form in file

Tank/Area	Date Inspected	Integrity of Containment Area Achieved	Source/Cause of Losses to Environment	Total Time of Containment Leakage	Quantity of Residues Removed	Notes
		☐ Yes ☐ No ☐ N/A	☐ Leak ☐ Damage ☐ Tear ☐ Block	☐ <30 min ☐ 1–2 hrs ☐ >2 hrs ☐ N/A	☐ None ☐ ____ drums ☐ N/A ☐ ____ gals	
		☐ Yes ☐ No ☐ N/A	☐ Leak ☐ Damage ☐ Tear ☐ Block	☐ <30 min ☐ 1–2 hrs ☐ >2 hrs ☐ N/A	☐ None ☐ ____ drums ☐ N/A ☐ ____ gals	
		☐ Yes ☐ No ☐ N/A	☐ Leak ☐ Damage ☐ Tear ☐ Block	☐ <30 min ☐ 1–2 hrs ☐ >2 hrs ☐ N/A	☐ None ☐ ____ drums ☐ N/A ☐ ____ gals	
		☐ Yes ☐ No ☐ N/A	☐ Leak ☐ Damage ☐ Tear ☐ Block	☐ <30 min ☐ 1–2 hrs ☐ >2 hrs ☐ N/A	☐ None ☐ ____ drums ☐ N/A ☐ ____ gals	
		☐ Yes ☐ No ☐ N/A	☐ Leak ☐ Damage ☐ Tear ☐ Block	☐ <30 min ☐ 1–2 hrs ☐ >2 hrs ☐ N/A	☐ None ☐ ____ drums ☐ N/A ☐ ____ gals	
		☐ Yes ☐ No ☐ N/A	☐ Leak ☐ Damage ☐ Tear ☐ Block	☐ <30 min ☐ 1–2 hrs ☐ >2 hrs ☐ N/A	☐ None ☐ ____ drums ☐ N/A ☐ ____ gals	
		☐ Yes ☐ No ☐ N/A	☐ Leak ☐ Damage ☐ Tear ☐ Block	☐ <30 min ☐ 1–2 hrs ☐ >2 hrs ☐ N/A	☐ None ☐ ____ drums ☐ N/A ☐ ____ gals	

CONTAINMENT SEALS

CONTAINMENT MATERIAL

VOLUME WASTE CONTAINED

CONTAINMENT ATTACHMENT

VOLUME USED

VOLUME LOST

CONTAINMENT AREA INTEGRITY REVIVIFIED

INSPECTED BY

DATE

REPORT #

ENVIRONMENTAL MANAGER REVIEW DATE

SUMMARY OF AMBIENT CONDITIONS

Reminder: Wind speed and direction can substantiate or relieve fault for alleged over-spray claims.

SUMMARY OF AMBIENT CONDITIONS

Date						Specific Location	
Time						Weather Conditions	
Air Temperature						Maximum Temperature	
Wet Bulb Temperature						Minimum Temperature	
Relative Humidity						Wind Speed	(MPH) ☐High ☐Med. ☐Low ☐Nil
Dew Point						Direction	
Steel Temperature						Remarks	

Date						Specific Location	
Time						Weather Conditions	
Air Temperature						Maximum Temperature	
Wet Bulb Temperature						Minimum Temperature	
Relative Humidity						Wind Speed	(MPH) ☐High ☐Med. ☐Low ☐Nil
Dew Point						Direction	
Steel Temperature						Remarks	

Date						Specific Location	
Time						Weather Conditions	
Air Temperature						Maximum Temperature	
Wet Bulb Temperature						Minimum Temperature	
Relative Humidity						Wind Speed	(MPH) ☐High ☐Med. ☐Low ☐Nil
Dew Point						Direction	
Steel Temperature						Remarks	
Report #							

SUMMARY OF AMBIENT CONDITIONS

Date						Specific Location	
Time						Weather Conditions	
Air Temperature						Maximum Temperature	
Wet Bulb Temperature						Minimum Temperature	
Relative Humidity						Wind Speed	(MPH) ☐High ☐Med. ☐Low ☐Nil
Dew Point						Direction	
Steel Temperature						Remarks	

Date						Specific Location	
Time						Weather Conditions	
Air Temperature						Maximum Temperature	
Wet Bulb Temperature						Minimum Temperature	
Relative Humidity						Wind Speed	(MPH) ☐High ☐Med. ☐Low ☐Nil
Dew Point						Direction	
Steel Temperature						Remarks	

Date						Specific Location	
Time						Weather Conditions	
Air Temperature						Maximum Temperature	
Wet Bulb Temperature						Minimum Temperature	
Relative Humidity						Wind Speed	(MPH) ☐High ☐Med. ☐Low ☐Nil
Dew Point						Direction	
Steel Temperature						Remarks	
Report #							

161

SUMMARY OF AMBIENT CONDITIONS

Date						Specific Location	
Time						Weather Conditions	
Air Temperature						Maximum Temperature	
Wet Bulb Temperature						Minimum Temperature	
Relative Humidity						Wind Speed	(MPH) ☐High ☐Med. ☐Low ☐Nil
Dew Point						Direction	
Steel Temperature						Remarks	

Date						Specific Location	
Time						Weather Conditions	
Air Temperature						Maximum Temperature	
Wet Bulb Temperature						Minimum Temperature	
Relative Humidity						Wind Speed	(MPH) ☐High ☐Med. ☐Low ☐Nil
Dew Point						Direction	
Steel Temperature						Remarks	

Date						Specific Location	
Time						Weather Conditions	
Air Temperature						Maximum Temperature	
Wet Bulb Temperature						Minimum Temperature	
Relative Humidity						Wind Speed	(MPH) ☐High ☐Med. ☐Low ☐Nil
Dew Point						Direction	
Steel Temperature						Remarks	
Report #							

SUMMARY OF AMBIENT CONDITIONS

Date						Specific Location	
Time						Weather Conditions	
Air Temperature						Maximum Temperature	
Wet Bulb Temperature						Minimum Temperature	
Relative Humidity						Wind Speed	(MPH) ☐High ☐Med. ☐Low ☐Nil
Dew Point						Direction	
Steel Temperature						Remarks	

Date						Specific Location	
Time						Weather Conditions	
Air Temperature						Maximum Temperature	
Wet Bulb Temperature						Minimum Temperature	
Relative Humidity						Wind Speed	(MPH) ☐High ☐Med. ☐Low ☐Nil
Dew Point						Direction	
Steel Temperature						Remarks	

Date						Specific Location	
Time						Weather Conditions	
Air Temperature						Maximum Temperature	
Wet Bulb Temperature						Minimum Temperature	
Relative Humidity						Wind Speed	(MPH) ☐High ☐Med. ☐Low ☐Nil
Dew Point						Direction	
Steel Temperature						Remarks	
Report #							

SUMMARY OF AMBIENT CONDITIONS

Date						Specific Location		
Time						Weather Conditions	
Air Temperature						Maximum Temperature	
Wet Bulb Temperature						Minimum Temperature	
Relative Humidity						Wind Speed	(MPH) ☐High ☐Med. ☐Low ☐Nil
Dew Point						Direction	
Steel Temperature						Remarks	

Date						Specific Location		
Time						Weather Conditions	
Air Temperature						Maximum Temperature	
Wet Bulb Temperature						Minimum Temperature	
Relative Humidity						Wind Speed	(MPH) ☐High ☐Med. ☐Low ☐Nil
Dew Point						Direction	
Steel Temperature						Remarks	

Date						Specific Location		
Time						Weather Conditions	
Air Temperature						Maximum Temperature	
Wet Bulb Temperature						Minimum Temperature	
Relative Humidity						Wind Speed	(MPH) ☐High ☐Med. ☐Low ☐Nil
Dew Point						Direction	
Steel Temperature						Remarks	
Report #							

SUMMARY OF AMBIENT CONDITIONS

Date						Specific Location	
Time						Weather Conditions	
Air Temperature						Maximum Temperature	
Wet Bulb Temperature						Minimum Temperature	
Relative Humidity						Wind Speed	(MPH) ☐High ☐Med. ☐Low ☐Nil
Dew Point						Direction	
Steel Temperature						Remarks	

Date						Specific Location	
Time						Weather Conditions	
Air Temperature						Maximum Temperature	
Wet Bulb Temperature						Minimum Temperature	
Relative Humidity						Wind Speed	(MPH) ☐High ☐Med. ☐Low ☐Nil
Dew Point						Direction	
Steel Temperature						Remarks	

Date						Specific Location	
Time						Weather Conditions	
Air Temperature						Maximum Temperature	
Wet Bulb Temperature						Minimum Temperature	
Relative Humidity						Wind Speed	(MPH) ☐High ☐Med. ☐Low ☐Nil
Dew Point						Direction	
Steel Temperature						Remarks	
Report #							

SUMMARY OF AMBIENT CONDITIONS

Date						Specific Location	
Time						Weather Conditions	
Air Temperature						Maximum Temperature	
Wet Bulb Temperature						Minimum Temperature	
Relative Humidity						Wind Speed	(MPH) ☐High ☐Med. ☐Low ☐Nil
Dew Point						Direction	
Steel Temperature						Remarks	

Date						Specific Location	
Time						Weather Conditions	
Air Temperature						Maximum Temperature	
Wet Bulb Temperature						Minimum Temperature	
Relative Humidity						Wind Speed	(MPH) ☐High ☐Med. ☐Low ☐Nil
Dew Point						Direction	
Steel Temperature						Remarks	

Date						Specific Location	
Time						Weather Conditions	
Air Temperature						Maximum Temperature	
Wet Bulb Temperature						Minimum Temperature	
Relative Humidity						Wind Speed	(MPH) ☐High ☐Med. ☐Low ☐Nil
Dew Point						Direction	
Steel Temperature						Remarks	
Report #							

SUMMARY OF AMBIENT CONDITIONS

Date							Specific Location		
Time							Weather Conditions		
Air Temperature							Maximum Temperature		
Wet Bulb Temperature							Minimum Temperature		
Relative Humidity							Wind Speed	(MPH) □High □Med. □Low □Nil	
Dew Point							Direction		
Steel Temperature							Remarks		

Date							Specific Location		
Time							Weather Conditions		
Air Temperature							Maximum Temperature		
Wet Bulb Temperature							Minimum Temperature		
Relative Humidity							Wind Speed	(MPH) □High □Med. □Low □Nil	
Dew Point							Direction		
Steel Temperature							Remarks		

Date							Specific Location		
Time							Weather Conditions		
Air Temperature							Maximum Temperature		
Wet Bulb Temperature							Minimum Temperature		
Relative Humidity							Wind Speed	(MPH) □High □Med. □Low □Nil	
Dew Point							Direction		
Steel Temperature							Remarks		
Report #									

SUMMARY OF AMBIENT CONDITIONS

Date						Specific Location			
Time						Weather Conditions			
Air Temperature						Maximum Temperature			
Wet Bulb Temperature						Minimum Temperature			
Relative Humidity						Wind Speed	(MPH) ☐High ☐Med. ☐Low ☐Nil		
Dew Point						Direction			
Steel Temperature						Remarks			

Date						Specific Location			
Time						Weather Conditions			
Air Temperature						Maximum Temperature			
Wet Bulb Temperature						Minimum Temperature			
Relative Humidity						Wind Speed	(MPH) ☐High ☐Med. ☐Low ☐Nil		
Dew Point						Direction			
Steel Temperature						Remarks			

Date						Specific Location			
Time						Weather Conditions			
Air Temperature						Maximum Temperature			
Wet Bulb Temperature						Minimum Temperature			
Relative Humidity						Wind Speed	(MPH) ☐High ☐Med. ☐Low ☐Nil		
Dew Point						Direction			
Steel Temperature						Remarks			

Report #	

SUMMARY OF AMBIENT CONDITIONS

Date						Specific Location		
Time						Weather Conditions		
Air Temperature						Maximum Temperature		
Wet Bulb Temperature						Minimum Temperature		
Relative Humidity						Wind Speed		(MPH) ☐High ☐Med. ☐Low ☐Nil
Dew Point						Direction		
Steel Temperature						Remarks		

Date						Specific Location		
Time						Weather Conditions		
Air Temperature						Maximum Temperature		
Wet Bulb Temperature						Minimum Temperature		
Relative Humidity						Wind Speed		(MPH) ☐High ☐Med. ☐Low ☐Nil
Dew Point						Direction		
Steel Temperature						Remarks		

Date						Specific Location		
Time						Weather Conditions		
Air Temperature						Maximum Temperature		
Wet Bulb Temperature						Minimum Temperature		
Relative Humidity						Wind Speed		(MPH) ☐High ☐Med. ☐Low ☐Nil
Dew Point						Direction		
Steel Temperature						Remarks		
Report #								

SUMMARY OF AMBIENT CONDITIONS

Date						Specific Location	
Time						Weather Conditions	
Air Temperature						Maximum Temperature	
Wet Bulb Temperature						Minimum Temperature	
Relative Humidity						Wind Speed	(MPH) ☐High ☐Med. ☐Low ☐Nil
Dew Point						Direction	
Steel Temperature						Remarks	

Date						Specific Location	
Time						Weather Conditions	
Air Temperature						Maximum Temperature	
Wet Bulb Temperature						Minimum Temperature	
Relative Humidity						Wind Speed	(MPH) ☐High ☐Med. ☐Low ☐Nil
Dew Point						Direction	
Steel Temperature						Remarks	

Date						Specific Location	
Time						Weather Conditions	
Air Temperature						Maximum Temperature	
Wet Bulb Temperature						Minimum Temperature	
Relative Humidity						Wind Speed	(MPH) ☐High ☐Med. ☐Low ☐Nil
Dew Point						Direction	
Steel Temperature						Remarks	
Report #							

SUMMARY OF AMBIENT CONDITIONS

Date						Specific Location	
Time						Weather Conditions	
Air Temperature						Maximum Temperature	
Wet Bulb Temperature						Minimum Temperature	
Relative Humidity						Wind Speed	(MPH) ☐High ☐Med. ☐Low ☐Nil
Dew Point						Direction	
Steel Temperature						Remarks	
Date						Specific Location	
Time						Weather Conditions	
Air Temperature						Maximum Temperature	
Wet Bulb Temperature						Minimum Temperature	
Relative Humidity						Wind Speed	(MPH) ☐High ☐Med. ☐Low ☐Nil
Dew Point						Direction	
Steel Temperature						Remarks	
Date						Specific Location	
Time						Weather Conditions	
Air Temperature						Maximum Temperature	
Wet Bulb Temperature						Minimum Temperature	
Relative Humidity						Wind Speed	(MPH) ☐High ☐Med. ☐Low ☐Nil
Dew Point						Direction	
Steel Temperature						Remarks	
Report #							

SUMMARY OF AMBIENT CONDITIONS

Date						Specific Location		
Time						Weather Conditions		
Air Temperature						Maximum Temperature		
Wet Bulb Temperature						Minimum Temperature		
Relative Humidity						Wind Speed		(MPH) ☐High ☐Med. ☐Low ☐Nil
Dew Point						Direction		
Steel Temperature						Remarks		

Date						Specific Location		
Time						Weather Conditions		
Air Temperature						Maximum Temperature		
Wet Bulb Temperature						Minimum Temperature		
Relative Humidity						Wind Speed		(MPH) ☐High ☐Med. ☐Low ☐Nil
Dew Point						Direction		
Steel Temperature						Remarks		

Date						Specific Location		
Time						Weather Conditions		
Air Temperature						Maximum Temperature		
Wet Bulb Temperature						Minimum Temperature		
Relative Humidity						Wind Speed		(MPH) ☐High ☐Med. ☐Low ☐Nil
Dew Point						Direction		
Steel Temperature						Remarks		
Report #								

SUMMARY OF AMBIENT CONDITIONS

Date						Specific Location				
Time						Weather Conditions				
Air Temperature						Maximum Temperature				
Wet Bulb Temperature						Minimum Temperature				
Relative Humidity						Wind Speed	(MPH) ☐High ☐Med. ☐Low ☐Nil			
Dew Point						Direction				
Steel Temperature						Remarks				

Date						Specific Location				
Time						Weather Conditions				
Air Temperature						Maximum Temperature				
Wet Bulb Temperature						Minimum Temperature				
Relative Humidity						Wind Speed	(MPH) ☐High ☐Med. ☐Low ☐Nil			
Dew Point						Direction				
Steel Temperature						Remarks				

Date						Specific Location				
Time						Weather Conditions				
Air Temperature						Maximum Temperature				
Wet Bulb Temperature						Minimum Temperature				
Relative Humidity						Wind Speed	(MPH) ☐High ☐Med. ☐Low ☐Nil			
Dew Point						Direction				
Steel Temperature						Remarks				
Report #										

SUMMARY OF AMBIENT CONDITIONS

Date						Specific Location	
Time						Weather Conditions	
Air Temperature						Maximum Temperature	
Wet Bulb Temperature						Minimum Temperature	
Relative Humidity						Wind Speed	(MPH) ☐High ☐Med. ☐Low ☐Nil
Dew Point						Direction	
Steel Temperature						Remarks	

Date						Specific Location	
Time						Weather Conditions	
Air Temperature						Maximum Temperature	
Wet Bulb Temperature						Minimum Temperature	
Relative Humidity						Wind Speed	(MPH) ☐High ☐Med. ☐Low ☐Nil
Dew Point						Direction	
Steel Temperature						Remarks	

Date						Specific Location	
Time						Weather Conditions	
Air Temperature						Maximum Temperature	
Wet Bulb Temperature						Minimum Temperature	
Relative Humidity						Wind Speed	(MPH) ☐High ☐Med. ☐Low ☐Nil
Dew Point						Direction	
Steel Temperature						Remarks	
Report #							

SUMMARY OF AMBIENT CONDITIONS

Date						Specific Location		
Time						Weather Conditions		
Air Temperature						Maximum Temperature		
Wet Bulb Temperature						Minimum Temperature		
Relative Humidity						Wind Speed	(MPH) □High □Med. □Low □Nil	
Dew Point						Direction		
Steel Temperature						Remarks		

Date						Specific Location		
Time						Weather Conditions		
Air Temperature						Maximum Temperature		
Wet Bulb Temperature						Minimum Temperature		
Relative Humidity						Wind Speed	(MPH) □High □Med. □Low □Nil	
Dew Point						Direction		
Steel Temperature						Remarks		

Date						Specific Location		
Time						Weather Conditions		
Air Temperature						Maximum Temperature		
Wet Bulb Temperature						Minimum Temperature		
Relative Humidity						Wind Speed	(MPH) □High □Med. □Low □Nil	
Dew Point						Direction		
Steel Temperature						Remarks		
Report #								

SUMMARY OF AMBIENT CONDITIONS

Date						Specific Location	
Time						Weather Conditions	
Air Temperature						Maximum Temperature	
Wet Bulb Temperature						Minimum Temperature	
Relative Humidity						Wind Speed	(MPH) ☐High ☐Med. ☐Low ☐Nil
Dew Point						Direction	
Steel Temperature						Remarks	

Date						Specific Location	
Time						Weather Conditions	
Air Temperature						Maximum Temperature	
Wet Bulb Temperature						Minimum Temperature	
Relative Humidity						Wind Speed	(MPH) ☐High ☐Med. ☐Low ☐Nil
Dew Point						Direction	
Steel Temperature						Remarks	

Date						Specific Location	
Time						Weather Conditions	
Air Temperature						Maximum Temperature	
Wet Bulb Temperature						Minimum Temperature	
Relative Humidity						Wind Speed	(MPH) ☐High ☐Med. ☐Low ☐Nil
Dew Point						Direction	
Steel Temperature						Remarks	
Report #							

SURFACE PREPARATION

SURFACE PREPARATION
Check off and document applicable items:

Job Title: _____

Specific Location: _____   Date: _____

☐ Bare Substrate   ☐ Oil & Grease   ☐ Laminations   ☐ Sharp Edges   ☐ Weld Spatter   ☐ Moisture   ☐ Rust   ☐ Soluble Salt   ☐ Lead or Heavy Metal

☐ Other _____

Corrections/Remarks _____

Type of Precleaning If Applicable: _____   Waterblast: _____   Pressure: _____

Abrasive Blast: _____   Specified Standard: _____   Abrasive Type: _____   Air Clean: _____

Nozzle Pressure: _____   Degree of Surface Cleaniness: _____

Nonconforming Items: _____

Specification Section: _____

Comments: _____
_____

Acceptable YES or NO: _____

Report # _____   (Circle One) **PASS** or **FAIL**

Surface Profile Avg. _____
(Reference Section V Page 315)

Start: _____

Finish: _____

Inspector's Initials: _____

SURFACE PREPARATION

Check off and document applicable items:

Job Title: _____

Specific Location: _____ Date: _____

☐ Bare Substrate ☐ Oil & Grease ☐ Laminations ☐ Sharp Edges ☐ Weld Spatter ☐ Moisture ☐ Rust ☐ Soluble Salt ☐ Lead or Heavy Metal

☐ Other _____

Corrections/Remarks _____

Type of Precleaning If Applicable: _____

Abrasive Blast: _____ Waterblast: _____ Pressure: _____

Specified Standard: _____ Abrasive Type: _____ Air Clean: _____

Nozzle Pressure: _____

Degree of Surface Cleaniness: _____

Nonconforming Items: _____

Specification Section: _____

Comments: _____

_____

Acceptable YES or NO: _____

Report # _____ (Circle One) **PASS** or **FAIL**

Surface Profile Avg. _____

(Reference Section V Page 315)

Start: _____

Finish: _____

Inspector's Initials: _____

179

SURFACE PREPARATION
Check off and document applicable items:

Job Title: _____

Specific Location: _____ Date: _____

☐ Bare Substrate ☐ Oil & Grease ☐ Laminations ☐ Sharp Edges ☐ Weld Spatter ☐ Moisture ☐ Rust ☐ Soluble Salt ☐ Lead or Heavy Metal

☐ Other _____

Corrections/Remarks _____

Type of Precleaning If Applicable: _____ Pressure: _____

Abrasive Blast: _____ Specified Standard: _____ Waterblast: _____ Abrasive Type: _____ Air Clean: _____

Nozzle Pressure: _____ Degree of Surface Cleaniness: _____

Nonconforming Items: _____

Surface Profile Avg. _____
(Reference Section V Page 315)

Specification Section: _____ **Start:** _____

Comments: _____ **Finish:** _____

_____

_____ **Inspector's Initials:** _____

Acceptable YES or NO: _____

Report # _____ *(Circle One)* **PASS** or **FAIL**

180

SURFACE PREPARATION
Check off and document applicable items:

Job Title: _____

Specific Location: _____ Date: _____

☐ Bare Substrate ☐ Oil & Grease ☐ Laminations ☐ Sharp Edges ☐ Weld Spatter ☐ Moisture ☐ Rust ☐ Soluble Salt ☐ Lead or Heavy Metal

☐ Other _____

Corrections/Remarks _____

Type of Precleaning If Applicable: _____

Abrasive Blast: _____ Specified Standard: _____ Waterblast: _____

Nozzle Pressure: _____ Degree of Surface Cleaniness: _____ Abrasive Type: _____ Pressure: _____

Nonconforming Items: _____

Specification Section: _____

Comments: _____
_____
_____

Acceptable YES or NO: _____

Report # _____ (Circle One) **PASS** or **FAIL**

Surface Profile Avg. _____
(Reference Section V Page 315)

Start: _____

Finish: _____

Inspector's Initials: _____

181

SURFACE PREPARATION

Check off and document applicable items:

Job Title: _____

Specific Location: _____ Date: _____

☐ Bare Substrate ☐ Oil & Grease ☐ Laminations ☐ Sharp Edges ☐ Weld Spatter ☐ Moisture ☐ Rust ☐ Soluble Salt ☐ Lead or Heavy Metal

☐ Other _____

Corrections/Remarks _____

Type of Precleaning If Applicable: _____

Abrasive Blast: _____ Specified Standard: _____ Waterblast: _____

Nozzle Pressure: _____ Degree of Surface Cleaniness: _____ Abrasive Type: _____ Pressure: _____

Nonconforming Items: _____ Air Clean: _____

Specification Section: _____

Comments: _____

_____

Acceptable YES or NO: _____

Report # _____ (Circle One) **PASS** or **FAIL**

| **Surface Profile Avg.** _____ |
| (Reference Section V Page 315) |
| **Start:** _____ |
| **Finish:** _____ |
| **Inspector's Initials:** _____ |

SURFACE PREPARATION

Check off and document applicable items:

Job Title: _____

Specific Location: _____ Date: _____

☐ Bare Substrate ☐ Oil & Grease ☐ Laminations ☐ Sharp Edges ☐ Weld Spatter ☐ Moisture ☐ Rust ☐ Soluble Salt ☐ Lead or Heavy Metal

☐ Other

Corrections/Remarks _____

Type of Precleaning If Applicable: _____

Abrasive Blast: _____ Waterblast: _____ Pressure: _____

Specified Standard: _____ Abrasive Type: _____ Air Clean: _____

Nozzle Pressure: _____

Degree of Surface Cleaniness: _____

Nonconforming Items: _____

Specification Section: _____

Comments: _____

_____

_____

Surface Profile Avg. _____
(Reference Section V Page 315)

Start: _____

Finish: _____

Inspector's Initials: _____

Acceptable YES or NO: _____

Report # _____ *(Circle One)* **PASS** or **FAIL**

SURFACE PREPARATION

Check off and document applicable items:

Job Title: _____

Specific Location: _____   Date: _____

☐ Bare Substrate   ☐ Oil & Grease   ☐ Laminations   ☐ Sharp Edges   ☐ Weld Spatter   ☐ Moisture   ☐ Rust   ☐ Soluble Salt   ☐ Lead or Heavy Metal

☐ Other _____

Corrections/Remarks _____

Type of Precleaning If Applicable: _____   Waterblast: _____   Pressure: _____

Abrasive Blast: _____   Specified Standard: _____   Abrasive Type: _____   Air Clean: _____

Nozzle Pressure: _____   Degree of Surface Cleanliness: _____

Nonconforming Items: _____

| Surface Profile Avg. _____ |
| *(Reference Section V Page 315)* |
| Start: _____ |
| Finish: _____ |
| Inspector's Initials: _____ |

Specification Section: _____

Comments: _____

_____

Acceptable YES or NO: _____

Report # _____   *(Circle One)* **PASS** or **FAIL**

184

SURFACE PREPARATION
Check off and document applicable items:

Job Title: _____

Specific Location: _____ Date: _____

☐ Bare Substrate ☐ Oil & Grease ☐ Laminations ☐ Sharp Edges ☐ Weld Spatter ☐ Moisture ☐ Rust ☐ Soluble Salt ☐ Lead or Heavy Metal

☐ Other _____

Corrections/Remarks _____

Type of Precleaning If Applicable: _____

Abrasive Blast: _____ Specified Standard: _____ Waterblast: _____ Pressure: _____

Nozzle Pressure: _____ Degree of Surface Cleaniness: _____ Abrasive Type: _____ Air Clean: _____

Nonconforming Items: _____

_____

Specification Section: _____

Comments: _____

_____

Acceptable YES or NO: _____

Report # _____ (Circle One) **PASS** or **FAIL**

Surface Profile Avg. _____
(Reference Section V Page 315)

Start: _____

Finish: _____

Inspector's Initials: _____

185

SURFACE PREPARATION

Check off and document applicable items:

Job Title: _____

Specific Location: _____   Date: _____

☐ Bare Substrate ☐ Oil & Grease ☐ Laminations ☐ Sharp Edges ☐ Weld Spatter ☐ Moisture ☐ Rust ☐ Soluble Salt ☐ Lead or Heavy Metal

☐ Other _____

Corrections/Remarks _____

Type of Precleaning If Applicable: _____   Waterblast: _____   Pressure: _____

Abrasive Blast: _____ Specified Standard: _____   Abrasive Type: _____   Air Clean: _____

Nozzle Pressure: _____ Degree of Surface Cleaniness: _____

Nonconforming Items: _____

Specification Section: _____

Comments: _____

_____

_____

Acceptable YES or NO: _____   (Circle One) **PASS** or **FAIL**

Report # _____

Surface Profile Avg. _____

(Reference Section V Page 315)

Start: _____

Finish: _____

Inspector's Initials: _____

186

SURFACE PREPARATION

Check off and document applicable items:

Job Title: _____

Specific Location: _____ Date: _____

☐ Bare Substrate ☐ Oil & Grease ☐ Laminations ☐ Sharp Edges ☐ Weld Spatter ☐ Moisture ☐ Rust ☐ Soluble Salt ☐ Lead or Heavy Metal

☐ Other _____

Corrections/Remarks _____

Type of Precleaning If Applicable: _____

Abrasive Blast: _____ Specified Standard: _____ Waterblast: _____

Nozzle Pressure: _____ Degree of Surface Cleaniness: _____ Abrasive Type: _____ Pressure: _____ Air Clean: _____

Nonconforming Items: _____
_____

Specification Section: _____

Comments: _____
_____
_____

Acceptable YES or NO: _____

Report # _____ (Circle One) **PASS** or **FAIL**

Surface Profile Avg. _____
(Reference Section V Page 315)

Start: _____

Finish: _____

Inspector's Initials: _____

187

SURFACE PREPARATION

Check off and document applicable items:

Job Title: _____

Specific Location: _____ Date: _____

☐ Bare Substrate ☐ Oil & Grease ☐ Laminations ☐ Sharp Edges ☐ Weld Spatter ☐ Moisture ☐ Rust ☐ Soluble Salt ☐ Lead or Heavy Metal

☐ Other _____

Corrections/Remarks _____

Type of Precleaning If Applicable: _____

Waterblast: _____ Pressure: _____

Abrasive Blast: _____ Specified Standard: _____ Abrasive Type: _____ Air Clean: _____

Nozzle Pressure: _____ Degree of Surface Cleaniness: _____

Nonconforming Items: _____

_____

Specification Section: _____

Comments: _____

_____

_____

Acceptable YES or NO: _____

Report # _____ (Circle One) **PASS** or **FAIL**

Surface Profile Avg. _____

(Reference Section V Page 315)

Start: _____

Finish: _____

Inspector's Initials: _____

SURFACE PREPARATION

Check off and document applicable items:

Job Title: _____ Date: _____

Specific Location: _____

☐ Bare Substrate ☐ Oil & Grease ☐ Laminations ☐ Sharp Edges ☐ Weld Spatter ☐ Moisture ☐ Rust ☐ Soluble Salt ☐ Lead or Heavy Metal

☐ Other _____

Corrections/Remarks _____

Type of Precleaning If Applicable: _____

Abrasive Blast: _____ Waterblast: _____ Pressure: _____

Specified Standard: _____

Nozzle Pressure: _____ Abrasive Type: _____ Air Clean: _____

Degree of Surface Cleaniness: _____

Nonconforming Items: _____

Surface Profile Avg. _____

(Reference Section V Page 315)

Specification Section: _____

Start: _____

Comments: _____

Finish: _____

_____

Inspector's Initials: _____

Acceptable YES or NO: _____

Report # _____ *(Circle One)* **PASS** or **FAIL**

SURFACE PREPARATION

Check off and document applicable items:

Job Title: _____ Date: _____

Specific Location: _____

☐ Bare Substrate ☐ Oil & Grease ☐ Laminations ☐ Sharp Edges ☐ Weld Spatter ☐ Moisture ☐ Rust ☐ Soluble Salt ☐ Lead or Heavy Metal

☐ Other _____

Corrections/Remarks _____

Type of Precleaning If Applicable: _____

Waterblast: _____ Pressure: _____

Abrasive Blast: _____ Specified Standard: _____ Abrasive Type: _____ Air Clean: _____

Nozzle Pressure: _____

Degree of Surface Cleaniness: _____

Nonconforming Items: _____

Specification Section: _____

Comments: _____

_____

Acceptable YES or NO: _____

Report # _____ (Circle One) **PASS** or **FAIL**

Surface Profile Avg.	
(Reference Section V Page 315)	
Start: _____	
Finish: _____	
Inspector's Initials: _____	

SURFACE PREPARATION

Check off and document applicable items:

Job Title: _____ Date: _____

Specific Location: _____

☐ Bare Substrate ☐ Oil & Grease ☐ Laminations ☐ Sharp Edges ☐ Weld Spatter ☐ Moisture ☐ Rust ☐ Soluble Salt ☐ Lead or Heavy Metal

☐ Other _____

Corrections/Remarks _____

Type of Precleaning If Applicable: _____

Abrasive Blast: _____ Waterblast: _____

Specified Standard: _____ Pressure: _____

Nozzle Pressure: _____ Abrasive Type: _____ Air Clean: _____

Degree of Surface Cleanliness: _____

Nonconforming Items: _____

| **Surface Profile Avg.** _____ |
| *(Reference Section V Page 315)* |
| **Start:** _____ |
| **Finish:** _____ |
| **Inspector's Initials:** _____ |

Specification Section: _____

Comments: _____

_____

_____

Acceptable YES or NO: _____

Report # _____ *(Circle One)* **PASS** or **FAIL**

191

SURFACE PREPARATION

Check off and document applicable items:

Job Title: _____

Specific Location: _____ Date: _____

☐ Bare Substrate ☐ Oil & Grease ☐ Laminations ☐ Sharp Edges ☐ Weld Spatter ☐ Moisture ☐ Rust ☐ Soluble Salt ☐ Lead or Heavy Metal

☐ Other

Corrections/Remarks _____

Type of Precleaning If Applicable: _____

Waterblast: _____ Pressure: _____

Abrasive Blast: _____ Specified Standard: _____ Abrasive Type: _____ Air Clean: _____

Nozzle Pressure: _____ Degree of Surface Cleanliness: _____

Nonconforming Items: _____

Specification Section: _____

Comments: _____

_____

Acceptable YES or NO: _____

Report # _____ (Circle One) **PASS** or **FAIL**

Surface Profile Avg.

(Reference Section V Page 315)

Start: _____

Finish: _____

Inspector's Initials: _____

SURFACE PREPARATION
Check off and document applicable items:

Job Title: _____ Date: _____

Specific Location: _____

☐ Bare Substrate ☐ Oil & Grease ☐ Laminations ☐ Sharp Edges ☐ Weld Spatter ☐ Moisture ☐ Rust ☐ Soluble Salt ☐ Lead or Heavy Metal

☐ Other _____

Corrections/Remarks _____

Type of Precleaning If Applicable: _____

Abrasive Blast: _____ Specified Standard: _____ Waterblast: _____ Pressure: _____

Nozzle Pressure: _____ Degree of Surface Cleaniness: _____ Abrasive Type: _____ Air Clean: _____

Nonconforming Items: _____
_____
_____

Surface Profile Avg. _____
(Reference Section V Page 315)

Start: _____

Finish: _____

Specification Section: _____

Comments: _____
_____
_____

Inspector's Initials: _____

Acceptable YES or NO: _____

Report # _____ *(Circle One)* **PASS** or **FAIL**

193

SURFACE PREPARATION
Check off and document applicable items:

Job Title: _____

Specific Location: _____ Date: _____

☐ Bare Substrate ☐ Oil & Grease ☐ Laminations ☐ Sharp Edges ☐ Weld Spatter ☐ Moisture ☐ Rust ☐ Soluble Salt ☐ Lead or Heavy Metal

☐ Other _____

Corrections/Remarks _____

Type of Precleaning If Applicable: _____

Waterblast: _____ Pressure: _____

Abrasive Blast: _____ Specified Standard: _____ Abrasive Type: _____ Air Clean: _____

Nozzle Pressure: _____ Degree of Surface Cleaniness: _____

Nonconforming Items: _____

Specification Section: _____

Comments: _____

_____

Acceptable YES or NO: _____

Report # _____ (Circle One) **PASS** or **FAIL**

Surface Profile Avg. _____
(Reference Section V Page 315)

Start: _____

Finish: _____

Inspector's Initials: _____

194

SURFACE PREPARATION
Check off and document applicable items:

Job Title: _____

Specific Location: _____ Date: _____

☐ Bare Substrate ☐ Oil & Grease ☐ Laminations ☐ Sharp Edges ☐ Weld Spatter ☐ Moisture ☐ Rust ☐ Soluble Salt ☐ Lead or Heavy Metal

☐ Other _____

Corrections/Remarks _____

Type of Precleaning If Applicable: _____

Abrasive Blast: _____ Specified Standard: _____ Waterblast: _____

Nozzle Pressure: _____ Degree of Surface Cleaniness: _____ Abrasive Type: _____ Pressure: _____

Nonconforming Items: _____ Air Clean: _____

Specification Section: _____

Comments: _____

_____

Acceptable YES or NO: _____

Report # _____ (Circle One) **PASS** or **FAIL**

┌─────────────────────────────────────┐
│ **Surface Profile Avg.** _____ │
│ *(Reference Section V Page 315)*   │
│   │
│ **Start:** _____   │
│   │
│ **Finish:** _____   │
│   │
│ **Inspector's Initials:** _____│
└─────────────────────────────────────┘

195

SURFACE PREPARATION

Check off and document applicable items:

Job Title: _____

Specific Location: _____   Date: _____

☐ Bare Substrate ☐ Oil & Grease ☐ Laminations ☐ Sharp Edges ☐ Weld Spatter ☐ Moisture ☐ Rust ☐ Soluble Salt ☐ Lead or Heavy Metal

☐ Other _____

Corrections/Remarks _____

Type of Precleaning If Applicable: _____

Abrasive Blast: _____   Specified Standard: _____   Waterblast: _____

Nozzle Pressure: _____   Degree of Surface Cleaniness: _____   Abrasive Type: _____   Pressure: _____   Air Clean: _____

Nonconforming Items: _____

Surface Profile Avg. _____

(Reference Section V Page 315)

Specification Section: _____

Comments: _____   **Start:** _____

_____   **Finish:** _____

_____

Acceptable YES or NO: _____   **Inspector's Initials:** _____

Report # _____   *(Circle One)* **PASS** or **FAIL**

196

SURFACE PREPARATION

Check off and document applicable items:

Job Title: _____

Specific Location: _____ Date: _____

☐ Bare Substrate ☐ Oil & Grease ☐ Laminations ☐ Sharp Edges ☐ Weld Spatter ☐ Moisture ☐ Rust ☐ Soluble Salt ☐ Lead or Heavy Metal

☐ Other _____

Corrections/Remarks _____

Type of Precleaning If Applicable: _____

Abrasive Blast: _____ Waterblast: _____ Pressure: _____

Specified Standard: _____ Abrasive Type: _____ Air Clean: _____

Nozzle Pressure: _____ Degree of Surface Cleaniness: _____

Nonconforming Items: _____

Specification Section: _____

Comments: _____

_____

Acceptable YES or NO: _____ (Circle One) **PASS** or **FAIL**

Report # _____

Surface Profile Avg. _____

(Reference Section V Page 315)

Start: _____

Finish: _____

Inspector's Initials: _____

197

SURFACE PREPARATION

Check off and document applicable items:

Job Title: _____

Specific Location: _____ Date: _____

☐ Bare Substrate ☐ Oil & Grease ☐ Laminations ☐ Sharp Edges ☐ Weld Spatter ☐ Moisture ☐ Rust ☐ Soluble Salt ☐ Lead or Heavy Metal

☐ Other _____

Corrections/Remarks _____

Type of Precleaning If Applicable: _____

Abrasive Blast: _____ Specified Standard: _____ Waterblast: _____ Pressure: _____

Nozzle Pressure: _____ Degree of Surface Cleaniness: _____ Abrasive Type: _____ Air Clean: _____

Nonconforming Items: _____

Surface Profile Avg. _____

(Reference Section V Page 315)

Specification Section: _____

Start: _____

Comments: _____

Finish: _____

_____

Acceptable YES or NO: _____ **Inspector's Initials:** _____

Report # _____ *(Circle One)* **PASS** or **FAIL**

SURFACE PREPARATION

Check off and document applicable items:

Job Title: _____

Specific Location: _____   Date: _____

☐ Bare Substrate ☐ Oil & Grease ☐ Laminations ☐ Sharp Edges ☐ Weld Spatter ☐ Moisture ☐ Rust ☐ Soluble Salt ☐ Lead or Heavy Metal

☐ Other _____

Corrections/Remarks _____

Type of Precleaning If Applicable: _____

Waterblast: _____   Pressure: _____

Abrasive Blast: _____   Specified Standard: _____   Abrasive Type: _____   Air Clean: _____

Nozzle Pressure: _____   Degree of Surface Cleaniness: _____

Noncoforming Items: _____

Surface Profile Avg. _____	
(Reference Section V Page 315)	
Start: _____	
Finish: _____	
Inspector's Initials: _____	

Specification Section: _____

Comments: _____

_____

Acceptable YES or NO: _____

Report # _____   *(Circle One)* **PASS** or **FAIL**

199

SURFACE PREPARATION
Check off and document applicable items:

Job Title: _____

Specific Location: _____ Date: _____

☐ Bare Substrate ☐ Oil & Grease ☐ Laminations ☐ Sharp Edges ☐ Weld Spatter ☐ Moisture ☐ Rust ☐ Soluble Salt ☐ Lead or Heavy Metal

☐ Other _____

Corrections/Remarks _____

Type of Precleaning If Applicable: _____ Waterblast: _____ Pressure: _____

Abrasive Blast: _____ Specified Standard: _____ Abrasive Type: _____ Air Clean: _____

Nozzle Pressure: _____ Degree of Surface Cleaniness: _____

Nonconforming Items: _____

Surface Profile Avg. _____
(Reference Section V Page 315)

Start: _____

Finish: _____

Inspector's Initials: _____

Specification Section: _____

Comments: _____

_____

_____

Acceptable YES or NO: _____

Report # _____ *(Circle One)* **PASS** or **FAIL**

SURFACE PREPARATION

Check off and document applicable items:

Job Title: _____

Date: _____

Specific Location: _____

☐ Bare Substrate ☐ Oil & Grease ☐ Laminations ☐ Sharp Edges ☐ Weld Spatter ☐ Moisture ☐ Rust ☐ Soluble Salt ☐ Lead or Heavy Metal

☐ Other

Corrections/Remarks _____

Type of Precleaning If Applicable: _____

Abrasive Blast: _____   Waterblast: _____

Specified Standard: _____   Pressure: _____

Nozzle Pressure: _____   Abrasive Type: _____   Air Clean: _____

Degree of Surface Cleaniness: _____

Nonconforming Items: _____

Specification Section: _____

Comments: _____

_____

Acceptable YES or NO: _____

Report # _____   (Circle One)   **PASS** or **FAIL**

Surface Profile Avg.
(Reference Section V Page 315)
Start: _____
Finish: _____
Inspector's Initials: _____

201

SURFACE PREPARATION

Check off and document applicable items:

Job Title: _____

Specific Location: _____ Date: _____

☐ Bare Substrate ☐ Oil & Grease ☐ Laminations ☐ Sharp Edges ☐ Weld Spatter ☐ Moisture ☐ Rust ☐ Soluble Salt ☐ Lead or Heavy Metal

☐ Other _____

Corrections/Remarks _____

Type of Precleaning If Applicable: _____

Waterblast: _____ Pressure: _____

Abrasive Blast: _____ Specified Standard: _____ Abrasive Type: _____ Air Clean: _____

Nozzle Pressure: _____ Degree of Surface Cleaniness: _____

Nonconforming Items: _____

_____

Specification Section: _____

Comments: _____

_____

Acceptable YES or NO: _____

Report # _____ (Circle One) **PASS** or **FAIL**

Surface Profile Avg. _____

(Reference Section V Page 315)

Start: _____

Finish: _____

Inspector's Initials: _____

SURFACE PREPARATION
Check off and document applicable items:

Job Title: _____

Specific Location: _____ Date: _____

☐ Bare Substrate ☐ Oil & Grease ☐ Laminations ☐ Sharp Edges ☐ Weld Spatter ☐ Moisture ☐ Rust ☐ Soluble Salt ☐ Lead or Heavy Metal

☐ Other _____

Corrections/Remarks _____

Type of Precleaning If Applicable: _____

Abrasive Blast: _____ Specified Standard: _____ Waterblast: _____ Pressure: _____

Nozzle Pressure: _____ Degree of Surface Cleanliness: _____ Abrasive Type: _____ Air Clean: _____

Nonconforming Items: _____

Specification Section: _____

Comments: _____
_____
_____

Acceptable YES or NO: _____ _____ (Circle One) **PASS** or **FAIL**

Report # _____

Surface Profile Avg. _____
(Reference Section V Page 315)

Start: _____

Finish: _____

Inspector's Initials: _____

203

SURFACE PREPARATION

Check off and document applicable items:

Job Title: _____

Specific Location: _____ Date: _____

☐ Bare Substrate ☐ Oil & Grease ☐ Laminations ☐ Sharp Edges ☐ Weld Spatter ☐ Moisture ☐ Rust ☐ Soluble Salt ☐ Lead or Heavy Metal

☐ Other _____

Corrections/Remarks _____

Type of Precleaning If Applicable: _____

Abrasive Blast: _____ Specified Standard: _____ Waterblast: _____ Pressure: _____

Nozzle Pressure: _____ Degree of Surface Cleaniness: _____ Abrasive Type: _____ Air Clean: _____

Nonconforming Items: _____

Surface Profile Avg. _____

(Reference Section V Page 315)

Specification Section: _____

Comments: _____

_____

Start: _____

Finish: _____

Acceptable YES or NO: _____

Inspector's Initials: _____

Report # _____ *(Circle One)* **PASS** or **FAIL**

SURFACE PREPARATION

Check off and document applicable items:

Job Title: _____

Specific Location: _____ Date: _____

☐ Bare Substrate ☐ Oil & Grease ☐ Laminations ☐ Sharp Edges ☐ Weld Spatter ☐ Moisture ☐ Rust ☐ Soluble Salt ☐ Lead or Heavy Metal

☐ Other _____

Corrections/Remarks _____

Type of Precleaning If Applicable: _____

Waterblast: _____ Pressure: _____

Abrasive Blast: _____ Specified Standard: _____ Abrasive Type: _____ Air Clean: _____

Nozzle Pressure: _____ Degree of Surface Cleaniness: _____

Nonconforming Items: _____

Specification Section: _____

Comments: _____

_____

Acceptable YES or NO: _____

Report # _____ (Circle One) **PASS** or **FAIL**

Surface Profile Avg. _____

(Reference Section V Page 315)

Start: _____

Finish: _____

Inspector's Initials: _____

205

SURFACE PREPARATION
Check off and document applicable items:

Job Title: _____

Specific Location: _____ Date: _____

☐ Bare Substrate ☐ Oil & Grease ☐ Laminations ☐ Sharp Edges ☐ Weld Spatter ☐ Moisture ☐ Rust ☐ Soluble Salt ☐ Lead or Heavy Metal

☐ Other

Corrections/Remarks _____

Type of Precleaning If Applicable: _____ Waterblast: _____ Pressure: _____

Abrasive Blast: _____ Specified Standard: _____ Abrasive Type: _____ Air Clean: _____

Nozzle Pressure: _____ Degree of Surface Cleaniness: _____

Nonconforming Items: _____

Specification Section: _____

Comments: _____

_____

Acceptable YES or NO: _____ (Circle One) **PASS** or **FAIL**

Report # _____

Surface Profile Avg. _____
(Reference Section V Page 315)

Start: _____

Finish: _____

Inspector's Initials: _____

206

SURFACE PREPARATION
Check off and document applicable items:

Job Title: _____

Specific Location: _____ Date: _____

☐ Bare Substrate ☐ Oil & Grease ☐ Laminations ☐ Sharp Edges ☐ Weld Spatter ☐ Moisture ☐ Rust ☐ Soluble Salt ☐ Lead or Heavy Metal

☐ Other _____

Corrections/Remarks _____

Type of Precleaning If Applicable: _____ Waterblast: _____

Abrasive Blast: _____ Specified Standard: _____ Abrasive Type: _____ Pressure: _____

Nozzle Pressure: _____ Degree of Surface Cleaniness: _____ Air Clean: _____

Nonconforming Items: _____

| Surface Profile Avg. _____ |
| *(Reference Section V Page 315)* |
| |
| Start: _____ |
| |
| Finish: _____ |
| |
| Inspector's Initials: _____ |

Specification Section: _____

Comments: _____

_____

_____

Acceptable YES or NO: _____

Report # _____ (*Circle One*) **PASS** or **FAIL**

SURFACE PREPARATION

Check off and document applicable items:

Job Title: _____

Specific Location: _____ Date: _____

☐ Bare Substrate ☐ Oil & Grease ☐ Laminations ☐ Sharp Edges ☐ Weld Spatter ☐ Moisture ☐ Rust ☐ Soluble Salt ☐ Lead or Heavy Metal

☐ Other _____

Corrections/Remarks _____

Type of Precleaning If Applicable: _____

Waterblast: _____ Pressure: _____

Abrasive Blast: _____ Specified Standard: _____ Abrasive Type: _____ Air Clean: _____

Nozzle Pressure: _____ Degree of Surface Cleanliness: _____

Nonconforming Items: _____

Surface Profile Avg. _____	
(Reference Section V Page 315)	
Start: _____	
Finish: _____	
Inspector's Initials: _____	

Specification Section: _____

Comments: _____

_____

_____

Acceptable YES or NO: _____

Report # _____   *(Circle One)* **PASS** or **FAIL**

208

SURFACE PREPARATION

Check off and document applicable items:

Job Title: _____

Specific Location: _____ Date: _____

☐ Bare Substrate ☐ Oil & Grease ☐ Laminations ☐ Sharp Edges ☐ Weld Spatter ☐ Moisture ☐ Rust ☐ Soluble Salt ☐ Lead or Heavy Metal

☐ Other _____

Corrections/Remarks _____

Type of Precleaning If Applicable: _____

Waterblast: _____ Pressure: _____

Abrasive Blast: _____ Specified Standard: _____

Nozzle Pressure: _____ Abrasive Type: _____ Air Clean: _____

Degree of Surface Cleaniness: _____

Nonconforming Items: _____

| Surface Profile Avg. _____ |
| *(Reference Section V Page 315)* |
| Start: _____ |
| Finish: _____ |
| Inspector's Initials: _____ |

Specification Section: _____

Comments: _____

_____

_____

Acceptable YES or NO: _____

Report # _____ *(Circle One)* **PASS** or **FAIL**

SURFACE PREPARATION

Check off and document applicable items:

Job Title: _____

Specific Location: _____   Date: _____

☐ Bare Substrate ☐ Oil & Grease ☐ Laminations ☐ Sharp Edges ☐ Weld Spatter ☐ Moisture ☐ Rust ☐ Soluble Salt ☐ Lead or Heavy Metal

☐ Other _____

Corrections/Remarks _____

Type of Precleaning If Applicable: _____   Waterblast: _____   Pressure: _____

Abrasive Blast: _____   Specified Standard: _____   Abrasive Type: _____   Air Clean: _____

Nozzle Pressure: _____   Degree of Surface Cleaniness: _____

Nonconforming Items: _____

_____

Specification Section: _____

Comments: _____

_____

Acceptable YES or NO: _____   (Circle One) **PASS** or **FAIL**

Report # _____

Surface Profile Avg. _____
(Reference Section V Page 315)

Start: _____

Finish: _____

Inspector's Initials: _____

210

INSPECTION OF COATING ON CONCRETE

NACE Coating Inspector's Logbook is primarily designed for use with structural steel coating work. However, many of the same inspection principles used in coating steel also apply when coating concrete. The following page contains the *minimum* inspection criteria an inspector should be familiar with when inspecting concrete.

MINIMUM FIELD CHECK LIST FOR COATING CONCRETE

Surface Preparation

1. Remove protrusions including but not limited to form lines, fins, sharp edges, corners, etc.

2. Fill bugholes, honeycombs, tie rod holes, and other voids

3. Remove laitance (thin, weak cement rich layer on concrete surface usually formed during finishing)

4. Remove effloresence (grayish white crystalline powdery deposit on surface)

5. Remove form release agents (see SSPC–SP 13/NACE 6 surface preparation for concrete)

6. Remove microbiological growths (25% solution household bleach to kill most organisms)

7. Test concrete soundness (ASTM D 4541 and ACI 503R)

8. Ensure specification requirements

9. Test air supply (ASTM D 4285)

10. Check for cleanliness and proper profile (see ICRI report # 03732)

11. Check for grease and oil

12. Perform chalking/dust wipe test (ASTM D 4214) or pressure sensitive tape test (ISO 8502-3)

13. Check etched surfaces for residual acid (ASTM D 4262)

14. Check moisture in concrete (ASTM D 4263) or (ASTM F 1869)

Coating Application

1. Check to see that all equipment is clean and working properly

2. Inspect color, gloss, and texture

3. Confirm that all mixing and application procedures conform too specified requirements

4. Check for amine blush, sags and runs

After Application

1. Check for cracks, blisters, and disbondment

2. Check thickness (ASTM D 4138)

3. Perform curing test (ASTM D 4752), (ASTM D 3363), (ASTM D 2240), or (ASTM D 2583)

4. Check coating adhesion (ASTM D 3359 or ASTM D 4541)

5. Check for discontinuities (ASTM D 4787)

SURFACE PREPARATION WITH
HIGH PRESSURE WATER
(AND OTHER METHODS USING WATER)

Forms in the *NACE Coating Inspector's Logbook* are compatible with multiple types of surface preparation including waterjetting. A checklist is provided to assist the inspector or coating foreman to check details they might otherwise overlook. Minimum requirements are listed. Persons should review all standards that are applicable. Several suggestions are recommended in this list.

MINIMUM FIELD CHECK LIST FOR SURFACE PREPARATION
WITH HIGH PRESSURE WATER AND OTHER METHODS USING WATER

Equipment & Safety

1. Safety check—see (DFR) Code of federal regulations (29 CFR 1926), (1926.62), (1926.20), (1926.21), (1926.59), (1926.103), (1926.104), (1926.105), (1926.451), (SSPC-Guide 6), (SSPC-Guide 61 con)
2. Proper spray tip for the job
3. Water pump maintenance
4. Pressure adequate
5. Coffer dam erected (if required)
6. HEPA vacuum equipment in place (if required)
7. Cascading storage tank or other in place (if required)

Surface Preparation

1. Review SSPC-SP-12 & SSPC-VIS 4 & NACE No. 7 also SSPC-TR2/NACE 6G198
2. Check for pre-existing surface profile (ASTM D 4417)
3. Review required disposal procedures for the area
4. Remove protrusions including but not limited to laminations, burrs, slivers, weld spatter, etc.
5. Fill porosity in welds
6. Ensure specification requirements
7. Check for cleanliness
8. Check for grease and oil
9. Check for chlorides and other contaminants

Coating Application

1. Check to see that all equipment is clean and working properly
2. Inspect color, gloss, and texture
3. Check to confirm that all mixing and application procedures conform to specified requirements
4. Check to confirm wet film thickness (ASTM 4414)
5. Check for amine blush, sags, and runs

After Application

1. Perform curing test (ASTM D 4752), (ASTM D 3363), (ASTM D 2240), or (ASTM D 2583)
2. Check dry paint measurement (SSPC-PA-2)
3. Check coating adhesion (ASTM D 3359 or ASTM D 4541)
4. Check for discontinuities (ASTM D 4787)

MIXING AND APPLICATION

MIXING AND APPLICATION GLOSSARY & INSTRUCTIONS

Date: Calendar date on which coating is applied

Location: Specific area coating is applied

Batch: A, B, & C Mfg. identification for individual product

Color: The color corresponding to batch & location

Mfg.: Coating manufacturer's name

Type: Coating product name

Coat #: First, second or third, etc.

High: Highest DFT reading

Low: Lowest DFT reading

Blk. Avg.: Average DFT from all blocks

Note: There are calculations to be made in accordance with SSPC PA-2 that are not applicable to this form. It is recommended to review the SSPC PA-2 standard before beginning job.

Refer to SSPC PA-2 for number of readings required in the areas exceeding 300 ft^2

Block instructions: Make 5 separate spot measurements (avg. 3 readings each) over each 100 ft^2 (9.3 m^2) area (reference SSPC PA-2) for a total of 15 individual readings. Place the final average DFT for each 100-300 ft^2 in one block.

MIXING AND APPLICATION

Job Title: _____ **Inspector:** _____ **Date:** _____

Caulk	☐ Yes	☐ No	Mixed	☐ Hand	☐ Power	Application	☐ Brush	☐ Spray	☐ Other

Spray — Other

Type ____ Thinner #/Type ____ Equipment Type ____

Mfg. Product Name/Number ____ % by Volume ____ Stripe Coat in Hard-to-Get Areas? ☐ Yes ☐ No

Induction Time ____ Supply Air Clean? ☐ Yes ☐ No Average WFT ____

Time: Start ____ Finish ____

Specific Location: ____

Average D.F.T. 100-300ft² per block (See SSPC-PA-2)

High D.F.T.	Low D.F.T.	Block Average	Remarks
Coat #	Manufacturer	Type	Color	Kit Size
Batch #	A	B	C	Gallons Used

Job Title: _____ **Inspector:** _____ **Date:** _____

Caulk	☐ Yes	☐ No	Mixed	☐ Hand	☐ Power	Application	☐ Brush	☐ Spray	☐ Other

Spray — Other

Type ____ Thinner #/Type ____ Equipment Type ____

Mfg. Product Name/Number ____ % by Volume ____ Stripe Coat in Hard-to-Get Areas? ☐ Yes ☐ No

Induction Time ____ Supply Air Clean? ☐ Yes ☐ No Average WFT ____

Time: Start ____ Finish ____

Specific Location: ____

Average D.F.T. 100-300ft² per block (See SSPC-PA-2)

High D.F.T.	Low D.F.T.	Block Average	Remarks
Coat #	Manufacturer	Type	Color	Kit Size
Batch #	A	B	C	Gallons Used

Report # ____ ☐ Pass ☐ Fail

MIXING AND APPLICATION

Block 1

Job Title:		Inspector:		Date:

Caulk ☐Yes ☐No	Mixed ☐Hand ☐Power	Application ☐Brush ☐Spray ☐Other	Spray	Other
Type	Thinner #/Type	Equipment Type		
Mfg. Product Name/Number	% by Volume	Stripe Coat in Hard-to-Get Areas?	☐Yes ☐No	
	Induction Time	Supply Air Clean? ☐Yes ☐No	Average WFT	
		Time: Start	Finish	

Specific Location:

Average D.F.T. 100-300ft² per block (See SSPC-PA-2)

High D.F.T.	Low D.F.T.	Block Average	Remarks	
Type	Manufacturer	Type	Color	Kit Size
Coat #				
Batch #	A	B	C	Gallons Used

Block 2

Job Title:		Inspector:		Date:

Caulk ☐Yes ☐No	Mixed ☐Hand ☐Power	Application ☐Brush ☐Spray ☐Other	Spray	Other
Type	Thinner #/Type	Equipment Type		
Mfg. Product Name/Number	% by Volume	Stripe Coat in Hard-to-Get Areas?	☐Yes ☐No	
	Induction Time	Supply Air Clean? ☐Yes ☐No	Average WFT	
		Time: Start	Finish	

Specific Location:

Average D.F.T. 100-300ft² per block (See SSPC-PA-2)

High D.F.T.	Low D.F.T.	Block Average	Remarks	
Type	Manufacturer	Type	Color	Kit Size
Coat #				
Batch #	A	B	C	Gallons Used

Report # | ☐ Pass ☐ Fail

MIXING AND APPLICATION

Job Title: _____ **Inspector:** _____ **Date:** _____

Caulk	☐ Yes	☐ No	Mixed	☐ Hand	☐ Power	Application	☐ Brush ☐ Spray ☐ Other	Spray	Other

Type | Thinner #/Type | Equipment Type |

Mfg. Product Name/Number | % by Volume | Stripe Coat in Hard-to-Get Areas? ☐ Yes ☐ No | ☐ Yes ☐ No

Induction Time | Supply Air Clean? ☐ Yes ☐ No | Average WFT

Time: Start _____ Finish _____

Specific Location: _____

Average D.F.T. 100-300ft² per block (See SSPC-PA-2)

High D.F.T.	Low D.F.T.	Block Average	Remarks

Coat #	Manufacturer	Type	Color	Kit Size

Batch #	A	B	C	Gallons Used

Job Title: _____ **Inspector:** _____ **Date:** _____

Caulk	☐ Yes	☐ No	Mixed	☐ Hand	☐ Power	Application	☐ Brush ☐ Spray ☐ Other	Spray	Other

Type | Thinner #/Type | Equipment Type |

Mfg. Product Name/Number | % by Volume | Stripe Coat in Hard-to-Get Areas? ☐ Yes ☐ No | ☐ Yes ☐ No

Induction Time | Supply Air Clean? ☐ Yes ☐ No | Average WFT

Time: Start _____ Finish _____

Specific Location: _____

Average D.F.T. 100-300ft² per block (See SSPC-PA-2)

High D.F.T.	Low D.F.T.	Block Average	Remarks

Coat #	Manufacturer	Type	Color	Kit Size

Batch #	A	B	C	Gallons Used

Report # _____   ☐ Pass   ☐ Fail

MIXING AND APPLICATION

Section 1

| Job Title: | | | | Inspector: | | Date: | |

Caulk	☐ Yes	☐ No		Application	☐ Brush ☐ Spray ☐ Other		
Type				Equipment Type			

Mfg. Product Name/Number

☐ Mixed	☐ Hand	☐ Power	☐ Spray	Other

Thinner #/Type		Stripe Coat in Hard-to-Get Areas?	☐ Yes	☐ No
% by Volume		Supply Air Clean?	☐ Yes	☐ No	Average WFT
Induction Time			Time: Start	Finish

Average D.F.T. 100-300ft² per block (See SSPC-PA-2)

Specific Location:

	High D.F.T.	Low D.F.T.	Block Average	Remarks
Coat #	Manufacturer		Type	Color	Kit Size
Batch #	A	B	C		Gallons Used

Section 2

| Job Title: | | | | Inspector: | | Date: | |

Caulk	☐ Yes	☐ No		Application	☐ Brush ☐ Spray ☐ Other		
Type				Equipment Type			

Mfg. Product Name/Number

☐ Mixed	☐ Hand	☐ Power	☐ Spray	Other

Thinner #/Type		Stripe Coat in Hard-to-Get Areas?	☐ Yes	☐ No
% by Volume		Supply Air Clean?	☐ Yes	☐ No	Average WFT
Induction Time			Time: Start	Finish

Average D.F.T. 100-300ft² per block (See SSPC-PA-2)

Specific Location:

	High D.F.T.	Low D.F.T.	Block Average	Remarks
Coat #	Manufacturer		Type	Color	Kit Size
Batch #	A	B	C		Gallons Used

Report #		☐ Pass	☐ Fail

MIXING AND APPLICATION

Form 1

| Job Title: | | | | | | | Inspector: | | | | Date: | |

Caulk: ☐ Yes ☐ No | Mixed ☐ Hand ☐ Power | Application ☐ Brush ☐ Spray ☐ Other | Spray | Other

Type | Thinner #/Type | Equipment Type

Mfg. Product Name/Number | % by Volume | Stripe Coat in Hard-to-Get Areas? ☐ Yes ☐ No

Induction Time | Supply Air Clean? ☐ Yes ☐ No ☐ Yes | Average WFT

Time: | Start | Finish

Specific Location:

Average D.F.T. 100-300ft² per block (See SSPC-PA-2)

High D.F.T.	Low D.F.T.	Block Average	Remarks	
Coat #	Manufacturer	Type	Color	Kit Size
Batch #	A	B	C	Gallons Used

Form 2

| Job Title: | | | | | | | Inspector: | | | | Date: | |

Caulk: ☐ Yes ☐ No | Mixed ☐ Hand ☐ Power | Application ☐ Brush ☐ Spray ☐ Other | Spray | Other

Type | Thinner #/Type | Equipment Type

Mfg. Product Name/Number | % by Volume | Stripe Coat in Hard-to-Get Areas? ☐ Yes ☐ No

Induction Time | Supply Air Clean? ☐ Yes ☐ No ☐ Yes | Average WFT

Time: | Start | Finish

Specific Location:

Average D.F.T. 100-300ft² per block (See SSPC-PA-2)

High D.F.T.	Low D.F.T.	Block Average	Remarks	
Coat #	Manufacturer	Type	Color	Kit Size
Batch #	A	B	C	Gallons Used

Report # | | ☐ Pass ☐ Fail

MIXING AND APPLICATION

Job Title: ___   Inspector: ___   Date: ___

Caulk	☐ Yes	☐ No	Mixed	☐ Hand	☐ Power	Application	☐ Brush ☐ Spray ☐ Other	Spray	Other
Type			Thinner #/Type			Equipment Type			
	Mfg. Product Name/Number		% by Volume			Stripe Coat in Hard-to-Get Areas?		☐ Yes	☐ No
			Induction Time			Supply Air Clean?	☐ Yes	☐ No	Average WFT

Time: ___ Start ___ Finish ___

Specific Location: ___

Average D.F.T. 100-300ft² per block (See SSPC-PA-2)

		Low D.F.T.		Block Average	Remarks		
High D.F.T.		Manufacturer		Type	Color		Kit Size
Coat #							
Batch #	A		B		C		Gallons Used

Job Title: ___   Inspector: ___   Date: ___

Caulk	☐ Yes	☐ No	Mixed	☐ Hand	☐ Power	Application	☐ Brush ☐ Spray ☐ Other	Spray	Other
Type			Thinner #/Type			Equipment Type			
	Mfg. Product Name/Number		% by Volume			Stripe Coat in Hard-to-Get Areas?		☐ Yes	☐ No
			Induction Time			Supply Air Clean?	☐ Yes	☐ No	Average WFT

Time: ___ Start ___ Finish ___

Specific Location: ___

Average D.F.T. 100-300ft² per block (See SSPC-PA-2)

		Low D.F.T.		Block Average	Remarks		
High D.F.T.		Manufacturer		Type	Color		Kit Size
Coat #							
Batch #	A		B		C		Gallons Used

Report # ___   ☐ Pass   ☐ Fail

227

MIXING AND APPLICATION

Form 1

Job Title:						Inspector:			Date:

Caulk: ☐Yes ☐No

Mixed: ☐Hand ☐Power

Application: ☐Brush ☐Spray ☐Other

| Type | Thinner #/Type | Equipment Type | Spray | Other |

Mfg. Product Name/Number | % by Volume | Stripe Coat in Hard-to-Get Areas? ☐Yes ☐No

| Induction Time | Supply Air Clean? ☐Yes ☐No | Average WFT |

Specific Location:

Time: Start ___ Finish ___

Average D.F.T. 100-300ft² per block (See SSPC-PA-2)

| High D.F.T. | Low D.F.T. | Block Average | Remarks |

| Coat # | Manufacturer | Type | Color | Kit Size |

| Batch # | A | B | C | Gallons Used |

Form 2

Job Title:						Inspector:			Date:

Caulk: ☐Yes ☐No

Mixed: ☐Hand ☐Power

Application: ☐Brush ☐Spray ☐Other

| Type | Thinner #/Type | Equipment Type | Spray | Other |

Mfg. Product Name/Number | % by Volume | Stripe Coat in Hard-to-Get Areas? ☐Yes ☐No

| Induction Time | Supply Air Clean? ☐Yes ☐No | Average WFT |

Specific Location:

Time: Start ___ Finish ___

Average D.F.T. 100-300ft² per block (See SSPC-PA-2)

| High D.F.T. | Low D.F.T. | Block Average | Remarks |

| Coat # | Manufacturer | Type | Color | Kit Size |

| Batch # | A | B | C | Gallons Used |

Report # ___ ☐Pass ☐Fail

MIXING AND APPLICATION

Job Title: _____ **Inspector:** _____ **Date:** _____

Caulk	☐Yes	☐No	Mixed	☐Hand	☐Power	Application	☐Brush ☐Spray ☐Other	Spray	Other

Type

Equipment Type

Thinner #/Type

Stripe Coat in Hard-to-Get Areas? ☐Yes ☐No

Mfg. Product Name/Number _____ % by Volume

Supply Air Clean? ☐Yes ☐No   Average WFT

Induction Time

Time: Start _____ Finish _____

Average D.F.T. 100-300ft² per block (See SSPC-PA-2)

Specific Location: _____

High D.F.T.	Low D.F.T.	Block Average	Remarks
Coat #	Manufacturer	Type	Color	Kit Size
Batch #	A	B	C	Gallons Used

Job Title: _____ **Inspector:** _____ **Date:** _____

Caulk	☐Yes	☐No	Mixed	☐Hand	☐Power	Application	☐Brush ☐Spray ☐Other	Spray	Other

Type

Equipment Type

Thinner #/Type

Stripe Coat in Hard-to-Get Areas? ☐Yes ☐No

Mfg. Product Name/Number _____ % by Volume

Supply Air Clean? ☐Yes ☐No   Average WFT

Induction Time

Time: Start _____ Finish _____

Average D.F.T. 100-300ft² per block (See SSPC-PA-2)

Specific Location: _____

High D.F.T.	Low D.F.T.	Block Average	Remarks
Coat #	Manufacturer	Type	Color	Kit Size
Batch #	A	B	C	Gallons Used

Report # _____   ☐Pass   ☐Fail

MIXING AND APPLICATION

Job Title:					Inspector:			Date:

Section 1

Caulk	☐ Yes	☐ No	Mixed	☐ Hand	☐ Power	Application	☐ Brush ☐ Spray ☐ Other	Spray	Other
Type			Thinner #/Type			Equipment Type			
Mfg. Product Name/Number			% by Volume			Stripe Coat in Hard-to-Get Areas?		☐ Yes	☐ No
			Induction Time			Supply Air Clean?	☐ Yes	☐ No	Average WFT

Time: Start / Finish

Specific Location:

Average D.F.T. 100-300ft² per block (See SSPC-PA-2)

High D.F.T.		Low D.F.T.		Block Average		Remarks	
Coat #		Manufacturer		Type		Color	Kit Size
Batch #	A		B		C		Gallons Used

Section 2

Job Title:					Inspector:			Date:

Caulk	☐ Yes	☐ No	Mixed	☐ Hand	☐ Power	Application	☐ Brush ☐ Spray ☐ Other	Spray	Other
Type			Thinner #/Type			Equipment Type			
Mfg. Product Name/Number			% by Volume			Stripe Coat in Hard-to-Get Areas?		☐ Yes	☐ No
			Induction Time			Supply Air Clean?	☐ Yes	☐ No	Average WFT

Time: Start / Finish

Specific Location:

Average D.F.T. 100-300ft² per block (See SSPC-PA-2)

High D.F.T.		Low D.F.T.		Block Average		Remarks	
Coat #		Manufacturer		Type		Color	Kit Size
Batch #	A		B		C		Gallons Used

Report #   ☐ Pass   ☐ Fail

MIXING AND APPLICATION

Job Title:					Inspector:			Date:	
Caulk	☐ Yes	☐ No	Mixed	☐ Hand	☐ Power	Application	☐ Brush ☐ Spray ☐ Other	Spray	Other
Type			Thinner #/Type			Equipment Type			
	Mfg. Product Name/Number		% by Volume			Stripe Coat in Hard-to-Get Areas?		☐ Yes	☐ No
			Induction Time			Supply Air Clean?	☐ Yes	☐ No	Average WFT
								Time: Start	Finish
Specific Location:					Average D.F.T. 100-300ft² per block (See SSPC-PA-2)				
High D.F.T.			Low D.F.T.		Block Average	Remarks			
Coat #			Manufacturer				Color	Kit Size	
Batch #	A		B			C			Gallons Used

Job Title:					Inspector:			Date:	
Caulk	☐ Yes	☐ No	Mixed	☐ Hand	☐ Power	Application	☐ Brush ☐ Spray ☐ Other	Spray	Other
Type			Thinner #/Type			Equipment Type			
	Mfg. Product Name/Number		% by Volume			Stripe Coat in Hard-to-Get Areas?		☐ Yes	☐ No
			Induction Time			Supply Air Clean?	☐ Yes	☐ No	Average WFT
								Time: Start	Finish
Specific Location:					Average D.F.T. 100-300ft² per block (See SSPC-PA-2)				
High D.F.T.			Low D.F.T.		Block Average	Remarks			
Coat #			Manufacturer				Color	Kit Size	
Batch #	A		B			C			Gallons Used
Report #			☐ Pass		☐ Fail				

231

MIXING AND APPLICATION

Job Title:					Inspector:			Date:

Caulk	☐Yes	☐No	Mixed	☐ Hand	☐ Power	Application	☐Brush ☐Spray ☐Other	Spray	Other

| Type | | | Thinner #/Type | | | Equipment Type | | | |

| Mfg. Product Name/Number | | | % by Volume | | | Stripe Coat in Hard-to-Get Areas? | | ☐ Yes | ☐ No |

| | | | Induction Time | | | Supply Air Clean? | ☐ Yes | ☐ No | Average WFT |

Time: Start | Finish

Average D.F.T. 100–300ft² per block (See SSPC-PA-2)

| Specific Location: | | | | | | | | | Gallons Used |

High D.F.T.		Low D.F.T.		Block Average		Remarks			
Coat #		Manufacturer			Type		Color	Kit Size	
Batch #	A		B			C			

Job Title:					Inspector:			Date:

Caulk	☐Yes	☐No	Mixed	☐ Hand	☐ Power	Application	☐Brush ☐Spray ☐Other	Spray	Other

| Type | | | Thinner #/Type | | | Equipment Type | | | |

| Mfg. Product Name/Number | | | % by Volume | | | Stripe Coat in Hard-to-Get Areas? | | ☐ Yes | ☐ No |

| | | | Induction Time | | | Supply Air Clean? | ☐ Yes | ☐ No | Average WFT |

Time: Start | Finish

Average D.F.T. 100–300ft² per block (See SSPC-PA-2)

| Specific Location: | | | | | | | | | Gallons Used |

High D.F.T.		Low D.F.T.		Block Average		Remarks			
Coat #		Manufacturer			Type		Color	Kit Size	
Batch #	A		B			C			

| Report # | | ☐ Pass | ☐ Fail |

MIXING AND APPLICATION

Job Title:						Inspector:			Date:
Caulk	☐ Yes	☐ No	Mixed	☐ Hand	☐ Power	Application	☐ Brush ☐ Spray ☐ Other	Spray	Other
Type			Thinner # /Type			Equipment Type			
Mfg. Product Name/Number			% by Volume			Stripe Coat in Hard-to-Get Areas?		☐ Yes	☐ No
			Induction Time			Supply Air Clean?	☐ Yes	☐ No	Average WFT
Specific Location:							Time:	Start	Finish

Average D.F.T. 100–300ft² per block (See SSPC-PA-2)

High D.F.T.		Low D.F.T.		Block Average	Remarks	
Coat #		Manufacturer		Type	Color	Kit Size
Batch #	A		B		C	Gallons Used

Job Title:						Inspector:			Date:
Caulk	☐ Yes	☐ No	Mixed	☐ Hand	☐ Power	Application	☐ Brush ☐ Spray ☐ Other	Spray	Other
Type			Thinner # /Type			Equipment Type			
Mfg. Product Name/Number			% by Volume			Stripe Coat in Hard-to-Get Areas?		☐ Yes	☐ No
			Induction Time			Supply Air Clean?	☐ Yes	☐ No	Average WFT
Specific Location:							Time:	Start	Finish

Average D.F.T. 100–300ft² per block (See SSPC-PA-2)

High D.F.T.		Low D.F.T.		Block Average	Remarks	
Coat #		Manufacturer		Type	Color	Kit Size
Batch #	A		B		C	Gallons Used
Report #			☐ Pass	☐ Fail		

MIXING AND APPLICATION

Form 1

Job Title:		Inspector:		Date:	

Caulk	☐ Yes	☐ No			
Type			Application	☐ Brush ☐ Spray ☐ Other	
Mfg. Product Name/Number			Equipment Type		
			Stripe Coat in Hard-to-Get Areas?	☐ Yes	☐ No
Mixed ☐ Hand ☐ Power			Supply Air Clean?	☐ Yes	☐ No
Thinner #/Type					
% by Volume				☐ Yes	☐ No
Induction Time			Time: Start		Finish
			Average WFT		

Average D.F.T. 100-300ft² per block (See SSPC-PA-2)

Specific Location: _____

	High D.F.T.	Low D.F.T.	Block Average	Remarks	
Coat #		Manufacturer		Color	Kit Size
Batch #	A	B		C	Gallons Used

Form 2

Job Title:		Inspector:		Date:	

Caulk	☐ Yes	☐ No			
Type			Application	☐ Brush ☐ Spray ☐ Other	
Mfg. Product Name/Number			Equipment Type		
			Stripe Coat in Hard-to-Get Areas?	☐ Yes	☐ No
Mixed ☐ Hand ☐ Power			Supply Air Clean?	☐ Yes	☐ No
Thinner #/Type					
% by Volume				☐ Yes	☐ No
Induction Time			Time: Start		Finish
			Average WFT		

Average D.F.T. 100-300ft² per block (See SSPC-PA-2)

Specific Location: _____

	High D.F.T.	Low D.F.T.	Block Average	Remarks	
Coat #		Manufacturer		Color	Kit Size
Batch #	A	B		C	Gallons Used
Report #		☐ Pass		☐ Fail	

MIXING AND APPLICATION

Job Title:				Inspector:			Date:

Caulk	☐Yes	☐No	☐Hand	Mixed	Spray	☐Power	Application	☐Brush ☐Spray ☐Other	Spray	Other

Type				Thinner #/Type			Equipment Type			

Mfg. Product Name/Number | % by Volume | Stripe Coat in Hard-to-Get Areas? ☐Yes ☐No

Induction Time | Supply Air Clean? ☐Yes ☐No | Average WFT

Time: Start | Finish

Specific Location:

Average D.F.T. 100-300ft^2 per block (See SSPC-PA-2)

	Low D.F.T.	High D.F.T.	Block Average	Remarks

Coat #	Manufacturer	Type	Color	Kit Size

Batch #	A	B	C	Gallons Used

Job Title:				Inspector:			Date:

Caulk	☐Yes	☐No	☐Hand	Mixed	Spray	☐Power	Application	☐Brush ☐Spray ☐Other	Spray	Other

Type				Thinner #/Type			Equipment Type			

Mfg. Product Name/Number | % by Volume | Stripe Coat in Hard-to-Get Areas? ☐Yes ☐No

Induction Time | Supply Air Clean? ☐Yes ☐No | Average WFT

Time: Start | Finish

Specific Location:

Average D.F.T. 100-300ft^2 per block (See SSPC-PA-2)

	Low D.F.T.	High D.F.T.	Block Average	Remarks

Coat #	Manufacturer	Type	Color	Kit Size

Batch #	A	B	C	Gallons Used

Report #	☐Pass	☐Fail

MIXING AND APPLICATION

Section 1

Job Title: _____   Inspector: _____   Date: _____

Caulk ☐ Yes ☐ No   Mixed ☐ Hand   Application ☐ Brush ☐ Spray ☐ Other   Spray   Other

Type _____   Equipment Type _____

Mfg. Product Name/Number _____   Thinner #/Type _____   % by Volume _____   Stripe Coat in Hard-to-Get Areas? ☐ Yes ☐ No

Induction Time _____   Supply Air Clean? ☐ Yes ☐ No   Average WFT

Specific Location: _____   Time: Start _____ Finish _____

Average D.F.T. 100-300ft² per block (See SSPC-PA-2)

High D.F.T.	Low D.F.T.	Block Average	Remarks
Coat #	Manufacturer	Type	Color	Kit Size
Batch #	A	B	C	Gallons Used

Section 2

Job Title: _____   Inspector: _____   Date: _____

Caulk ☐ Yes ☐ No   Mixed ☐ Hand   Application ☐ Brush ☐ Spray ☐ Other   Spray   Other

Type _____   Equipment Type _____

Mfg. Product Name/Number _____   Thinner #/Type _____   % by Volume _____   Stripe Coat in Hard-to-Get Areas? ☐ Yes ☐ No

Induction Time _____   Supply Air Clean? ☐ Yes ☐ No   Average WFT

Specific Location: _____   Time: Start _____ Finish _____

Average D.F.T. 100-300ft² per block (See SSPC-PA-2)

High D.F.T.	Low D.F.T.	Block Average	Remarks
Coat #	Manufacturer	Type	Color	Kit Size
Batch #	A	B	C	Gallons Used

Report # _____   ☐ Pass   ☐ Fail

236

MIXING AND APPLICATION

Section 1

Job Title:				Inspector:			Date:	
Caulk	☐Yes	☐No	☐ Hand	☐ Power	Application	☐Brush ☐Spray ☐Other	Spray	Other
Type					Equipment Type			
		Thinner #/Type			Stripe Coat in Hard-to-Get Areas?		☐ Yes	☐ No
Mfg. Product Name/Number		% by Volume			Supply Air Clean?	☐ Yes	☐ No	Average WFT
		Induction Time					Time: Start	Finish

Average D.F.T. 100–300ft² per block (See SSPC-PA-2)

	Low D.F.T.		Block Average		Remarks			
High D.F.T.	Manufacturer		Type		Color		Kit Size	
Coat #								
Batch #	A		B		C			Gallons Used

Specific Location:

Section 2

Job Title:				Inspector:			Date:	
Caulk	☐Yes	☐No	☐ Hand	☐ Power	Application	☐Brush ☐Spray ☐Other	Spray	Other
Type					Equipment Type			
		Thinner #/Type			Stripe Coat in Hard-to-Get Areas?		☐ Yes	☐ No
Mfg. Product Name/Number		% by Volume			Supply Air Clean?	☐ Yes	☐ No	Average WFT
		Induction Time					Time: Start	Finish

Average D.F.T. 100–300ft² per block (See SSPC-PA-2)

	Low D.F.T.		Block Average		Remarks			
High D.F.T.	Manufacturer		Type		Color		Kit Size	
Coat #								
Batch #	A		B		C			Gallons Used
Report #			☐ Pass	☐ Fail				

Specific Location:

237

MIXING AND APPLICATION

Section 1

Job Title:					Inspector:			Date:

Caulk	☐Yes	☐No	Mixed	☐Hand	☐Power	Application	☐Brush ☐Spray ☐Other	Spray	Other

| Type | | | Thinner #/Type | | | Equipment Type | | | |

| Mfg. Product Name/Number | | | % by Volume | | | Stripe Coat in Hard-to-Get Areas? | | ☐Yes | ☐No |

| | | | Induction Time | | | Supply Air Clean? | ☐Yes | ☐No | Average WFT |

Specific Location:

Average D.F.T. 100-300ft² per block (See SSPC-PA-2)

Time: | Start | Finish

High D.F.T.		Low D.F.T.		Block Average		Remarks			

| Coat # | | Manufacturer | | Type | | Color | | Kit Size | |

| Batch # | A | | B | | | C | | Gallons Used | |

Section 2

Job Title:					Inspector:			Date:

Caulk	☐Yes	☐No	Mixed	☐Hand	☐Power	Application	☐Brush ☐Spray ☐Other	Spray	Other

| Type | | | Thinner #/Type | | | Equipment Type | | | |

| Mfg. Product Name/Number | | | % by Volume | | | Stripe Coat in Hard-to-Get Areas? | | ☐Yes | ☐No |

| | | | Induction Time | | | Supply Air Clean? | ☐Yes | ☐No | Average WFT |

Specific Location:

Average D.F.T. 100-300ft² per block (See SSPC-PA-2)

Time: | Start | Finish

High D.F.T.		Low D.F.T.		Block Average		Remarks			

| Coat # | | Manufacturer | | Type | | Color | | Kit Size | |

| Batch # | A | | B | | | C | | Gallons Used | |

| Report # | | | ☐Pass | ☐Fail | |

MIXING AND APPLICATION

Section 1

Job Title:		Inspector:		Date:	

Caulk	☐Yes	☐No		Application	☐Brush ☐Spray ☐Other	Spray	Other
Type				Equipment Type			

Mfg. Product Name/Number

Stripe Coat in Hard-to-Get Areas?	☐Yes	☐No

Mixed	☐Hand	☐Power
Thinner #/Type		
% by Volume		
Induction Time		

Supply Air Clean?	☐Yes	☐No

Average WFT

Time: Start ___ Finish ___

Specific Location:

Average D.F.T. 100–300ft² per block (See SSPC-PA-2)

	High D.F.T.	Low D.F.T.	Block Average	Remarks
Coat #		Manufacturer	Type	Color	Kit Size
Batch #	A	B	C	Gallons Used

Section 2

Job Title:		Inspector:		Date:	

Caulk	☐Yes	☐No		Application	☐Brush ☐Spray ☐Other	Spray	Other
Type				Equipment Type			

Mfg. Product Name/Number

Stripe Coat in Hard-to-Get Areas?	☐Yes	☐No

Mixed	☐Hand	☐Power
Thinner #/Type		
% by Volume		
Induction Time		

Supply Air Clean?	☐Yes	☐No

Average WFT

Time: Start ___ Finish ___

Specific Location:

Average D.F.T. 100–300ft² per block (See SSPC-PA-2)

	High D.F.T.	Low D.F.T.	Block Average	Remarks
Coat #		Manufacturer	Type	Color	Kit Size
Batch #	A	B	C	Gallons Used

Report # ___ ☐ Pass ☐ Fail

MIXING AND APPLICATION

Job Title:						Inspector:				Date:

Caulk	☐ Yes	☐ No	Mixed	☐ Hand	☐ Power	Application	☐ Brush ☐ Spray ☐ Other	Spray		Other
Type			Thinner #/Type			Equipment Type				
Mfg. Product Name/Number			% by Volume			Stripe Coat in Hard-to-Get Areas?			☐ Yes	☐ No
			Induction Time			Supply Air Clean?	☐ Yes	☐ No	Average WFT	
								Time:	Start	Finish

Average D.F.T. 100-300ft² per block (See SSPC-PA-2)

Specific Location:										
High D.F.T.			Low D.F.T.		Block Average		Remarks			
Coat #			Manufacturer		Type		Color		Kit Size	
Batch #		A		B		C				Gallons Used

Job Title:						Inspector:				Date:

Caulk	☐ Yes	☐ No	Mixed	☐ Hand	☐ Power	Application	☐ Brush ☐ Spray ☐ Other	Spray		Other
Type			Thinner #/Type			Equipment Type				
Mfg. Product Name/Number			% by Volume			Stripe Coat in Hard-to-Get Areas?			☐ Yes	☐ No
			Induction Time			Supply Air Clean?	☐ Yes	☐ No	Average WFT	
								Time:	Start	Finish

Average D.F.T. 100-300ft² per block (See SSPC-PA-2)

Specific Location:										
High D.F.T.			Low D.F.T.		Block Average		Remarks			
Coat #			Manufacturer		Type		Color		Kit Size	
Batch #		A		B		C				Gallons Used

Report #			☐ Pass		☐ Fail					

MIXING AND APPLICATION

Section 1

Job Title:				Inspector:			Date:

Caulk	□Yes	□No	Mixed	□Hand	□Power	Application	□Brush □Spray □Other	Spray	Other
Type			Thinner #/Type			Equipment Type			
Mfg. Product Name/Number			% by Volume			Stripe Coat in Hard-to-Get Areas?		□Yes	□No
			Induction Time			Supply Air Clean?	□Yes	□No	Average WFT

Time: Start _____ Finish _____

Specific Location: _____

Average D.F.T. 100-300ft² per block (See SSPC-PA-2)

	High D.F.T.	Low D.F.T.	Block Average	Remarks
Coat #	Manufacturer	Type	Color	Kit Size
Batch #	A	B	C	Gallons Used

Section 2

Job Title:				Inspector:			Date:

Caulk	□Yes	□No	Mixed	□Hand	□Power	Application	□Brush □Spray □Other	Spray	Other
Type			Thinner #/Type			Equipment Type			
Mfg. Product Name/Number			% by Volume			Stripe Coat in Hard-to-Get Areas?		□Yes	□No
			Induction Time			Supply Air Clean?	□Yes	□No	Average WFT

Time: Start _____ Finish _____

Specific Location: _____

Average D.F.T. 100-300ft² per block (See SSPC-PA-2)

	High D.F.T.	Low D.F.T.	Block Average	Remarks
Coat #	Manufacturer	Type	Color	Kit Size
Batch #	A	B	C	Gallons Used

Report # _____   □Pass   □Fail

MIXING AND APPLICATION

Form 1

Job Title:		Inspector:		Date:	

Caulk	☐ Yes	☐ No	Mixed	☐ Hand	☐ Power	Application	☐ Brush	☐ Spray	☐ Other	Spray	Other

| Type | | | Thinner #/Type | | | Equipment Type | | | | |

Mfg. Product Name/Number		% by Volume		Stripe Coat in Hard-to-Get Areas?	☐ Yes	☐ No

| | | Induction Time | | Supply Air Clean? | ☐ Yes | ☐ No | Average WFT |

Specific Location:		Time:	Start	Finish

Average D.F.T. 100-300ft² per block (See SSPC-PA-2)

High D.F.T.		Low D.F.T.		Block Average	Remarks
Coat #		Manufacturer		Color	Kit Size
Batch #	A	B	C		Gallons Used

Form 2

Job Title:		Inspector:		Date:	

Caulk	☐ Yes	☐ No	Mixed	☐ Hand	☐ Power	Application	☐ Brush	☐ Spray	☐ Other	Spray	Other

| Type | | | Thinner #/Type | | | Equipment Type | | | | |

Mfg. Product Name/Number		% by Volume		Stripe Coat in Hard-to-Get Areas?	☐ Yes	☐ No

| | | Induction Time | | Supply Air Clean? | ☐ Yes | ☐ No | Average WFT |

Specific Location:		Time:	Start	Finish

Average D.F.T. 100-300ft² per block (See SSPC-PA-2)

High D.F.T.		Low D.F.T.		Block Average	Remarks
Coat #		Manufacturer		Color	Kit Size
Batch #	A	B	C		Gallons Used
Report #			☐ Pass	☐ Fail	

MIXING AND APPLICATION

Section 1

Job Title:					Inspector:				Date:

Caulk	☐ Yes	☐ No	Mixed	☐ Hand	☐ Power	Application	☐ Brush ☐ Spray ☐ Other	Spray	Other

| Type | | | Thinner #/Type | | | Equipment Type | | | |

| Mfg. Product Name/Number | | | % by Volume | | | Stripe Coat in Hard-to-Get Areas? | | ☐ Yes | ☐ No |

| | | | Induction Time | | | Supply Air Clean? | ☐ Yes | ☐ No | Average WFT |

| | | | | | | | Time: | Start | Finish |

Specific Location:

Average D.F.T. 100-300ft² per block (See SSPC-PA-2)

High D.F.T.		Low D.F.T.		Block Average		Remarks			

| Type | | Manufacturer | | Type | | Color | | Kit Size | |

| Batch # | | A | | B | | C | | | Gallons Used |

Section 2

Job Title:					Inspector:				Date:

Caulk	☐ Yes	☐ No	Mixed	☐ Hand	☐ Power	Application	☐ Brush ☐ Spray ☐ Other	Spray	Other

| Type | | | Thinner #/Type | | | Equipment Type | | | |

| Mfg. Product Name/Number | | | % by Volume | | | Stripe Coat in Hard-to-Get Areas? | | ☐ Yes | ☐ No |

| | | | Induction Time | | | Supply Air Clean? | ☐ Yes | ☐ No | Average WFT |

| | | | | | | | Time: | Start | Finish |

Specific Location:

Average D.F.T. 100-300ft² per block (See SSPC-PA-2)

High D.F.T.		Low D.F.T.		Block Average		Remarks			

| Type | | Manufacturer | | Type | | Color | | Kit Size | |

| Batch # | | A | | B | | C | | | Gallons Used |

| Report # | | | ☐ Pass | ☐ Fail | | | | | |

MIXING AND APPLICATION

Section 1

Job Title: _____   Inspector: _____   Date: _____

Caulk   ☐ Yes   ☐ No

	Mixed	☐ Hand	☐ Power	Application	☐ Brush ☐ Spray ☐ Other	Spray	Other

Type _____   Thinner #/Type _____   Equipment Type _____

Mfg. Product Name/Number _____   % by Volume _____   Stripe Coat in Hard-to-Get Areas?   ☐ Yes   ☐ No

Induction Time _____   Supply Air Clean?   ☐ Yes   ☐ No   Average WFT _____

Time: Start _____   Finish _____

Specific Location: _____

Average D.F.T. 100–300ft² per block (See SSPC-PA-2)

High D.F.T.		Low D.F.T.		Block Average	Remarks	

Coat # _____   Manufacturer _____   Type _____   Color _____   Kit Size _____

Batch #   A _____   B _____   C _____   Gallons Used _____

Section 2

Job Title: _____   Inspector: _____   Date: _____

Caulk   ☐ Yes   ☐ No

	Mixed	☐ Hand	☐ Power	Application	☐ Brush ☐ Spray ☐ Other	Spray	Other

Type _____   Thinner #/Type _____   Equipment Type _____

Mfg. Product Name/Number _____   % by Volume _____   Stripe Coat in Hard-to-Get Areas?   ☐ Yes   ☐ No

Induction Time _____   Supply Air Clean?   ☐ Yes   ☐ No   Average WFT _____

Time: Start _____   Finish _____

Specific Location: _____

Average D.F.T. 100–300ft² per block (See SSPC-PA-2)

High D.F.T.		Low D.F.T.		Block Average	Remarks	

Coat # _____   Manufacturer _____   Type _____   Color _____   Kit Size _____

Batch #   A _____   B _____   C _____   Gallons Used _____

Report #   ☐ Pass   ☐ Fail

244

DAILY PRODUCTION RECORD

DAILY PRODUCTION RECORD

Job Title:

Specific Location:

Date	Area(s) Worked	Personnel on Site (Number)	Surface Preparation Staff Hrs./Ft^2	Painting Staff Hrs./Ft^2	Rigging/Scaffolding Staff Hrs./Ft^2	Inspection By

Report #

DAILY PRODUCTION RECORD

Job Title:

Specific Location:

Date	Area(s) Worked	Personnel on Site (Number)	Surface Preparation Staff Hrs./Ft^2	Painting Staff Hrs./Ft^2	Rigging/Scaffolding Staff Hrs./Ft^2	Inspection By

Report #

DAILY PRODUCTION RECORD

Job Title: _____   **Specific Location:** _____

Date	Area(s) Worked	Personnel on Site (Number)	Surface Preparation Staff Hrs./Ft^2	Painting Staff Hrs./Ft^2	Rigging/Scaffolding Staff Hrs./Ft^2	Inspection By

Report # _____

DAILY PRODUCTION RECORD

Job Title: **Specific Location:**

Date	Area(s) Worked	Personnel on Site (Number)	Surface Preparation Staff Hrs./Ft²	Painting Staff Hrs./Ft²	Rigging/Scaffolding Staff Hrs./Ft²	Inspection By

Report #

249

DAILY PRODUCTION RECORD

Job Title:

Specific Location:

Date	Area(s) Worked	Personnel on Site (Number)	Surface Preparation Staff Hrs./Ft^2	Painting Staff Hrs./Ft^2	Rigging/Scaffolding Staff Hrs./Ft^2	Inspection By

Report #

SECTION III
INSPECTOR'S DAILY LOG

THE INSPECTOR'S DAILY LOG

The *NACE Coating Inspector's Logbook* is a compilation of information with a designated area for daily entries. Since no one form or book can meet every need, the daily log is necessary. The inspector/foreman should use this section to note details that do not fit elsewhere. It is important to use as much space as necessary; hence, the date is optional. For future reference it is helpful to initial each entry. Do not use pencil.

See: Coating Inspector's Check List Page 10

INSPECTOR'S DAILY LOG

DATE:	
COMMENTS:	

REPORT #:

DATE:	
COMMENTS:	

REPORT #:

INSPECTOR'S DAILY LOG

DATE:

COMMENTS:

REPORT #:

DATE:

COMMENTS:

REPORT #:

INSPECTOR'S DAILY LOG

DATE:	
COMMENTS:	

REPORT #:

DATE:	
COMMENTS:	

REPORT #:

INSPECTOR'S DAILY LOG

DATE:

COMMENTS:

REPORT #:

DATE:

COMMENTS:

REPORT #:

INSPECTOR'S DAILY LOG

DATE:	
COMMENTS:	

REPORT #:

DATE:	
COMMENTS:	

REPORT #:

INSPECTOR'S DAILY LOG

DATE:

COMMENTS:

REPORT #:

DATE:

COMMENTS:

REPORT #:

INSPECTOR'S DAILY LOG

DATE:	
COMMENTS:	

REPORT #:	

DATE:	
COMMENTS:	

REPORT #:	

INSPECTOR'S DAILY LOG

DATE:

COMMENTS:

REPORT #:

DATE:

COMMENTS:

REPORT #:

INSPECTOR'S DAILY LOG

DATE:	
COMMENTS:	

REPORT #:

DATE:	
COMMENTS:	

REPORT #:

INSPECTOR'S DAILY LOG

DATE:

COMMENTS:

REPORT #:

DATE:

COMMENTS:

REPORT #:

INSPECTOR'S DAILY LOG

DATE:	
COMMENTS:	

REPORT #:	

DATE:	
COMMENTS:	

REPORT #:	

INSPECTOR'S DAILY LOG

DATE:

COMMENTS:

REPORT #:

DATE:

COMMENTS:

REPORT #:

INSPECTOR'S DAILY LOG

DATE:

COMMENTS:

REPORT #:

DATE:

COMMENTS:

REPORT #:

INSPECTOR'S DAILY LOG

DATE:

COMMENTS:

REPORT #:

DATE:

COMMENTS:

REPORT #:

INSPECTOR'S DAILY LOG

DATE:	
COMMENTS:	

REPORT #:

DATE:	
COMMENTS:	

REPORT #:

INSPECTOR'S DAILY LOG

DATE:

COMMENTS:

REPORT #:

DATE:

COMMENTS:

REPORT #:

INSPECTOR'S DAILY LOG

DATE:

COMMENTS:

REPORT #:

DATE:

COMMENTS:

REPORT #:

INSPECTOR'S DAILY LOG

DATE:

COMMENTS:

REPORT #:

DATE:

COMMENTS:

REPORT #:

INSPECTOR'S DAILY LOG

DATE:	
COMMENTS:	

REPORT #:	

DATE:	
COMMENTS:	

REPORT #:	

INSPECTOR'S DAILY LOG

DATE:

COMMENTS:

REPORT #:

DATE:

COMMENTS:

REPORT #:

INSPECTOR'S DAILY LOG

DATE:

COMMENTS:

REPORT #:

DATE:

COMMENTS:

REPORT #:

INSPECTOR'S DAILY LOG

DATE:

COMMENTS:

REPORT #:

DATE:

COMMENTS:

REPORT #:

INSPECTOR'S DAILY LOG

DATE:

COMMENTS:

REPORT #:

DATE:

COMMENTS:

REPORT #:

JOB COMPLETION FORM

JOB COMPLETION FORM

Job Number:	Date:
Customer:	P.O. Number:

Job Description:

The above job has been completed in an acceptable manner and may be billed as 100% complete.

Company Representative	Customer Representative

JOB COMPLETION FORM

Job Number:	Date:
Customer:	P.O. Number:

Job Description:

The above job has been completed in an acceptable manner and may be billed as 100% complete.

Company Representative	Customer Representative

JOB COMPLETION FORM

Job Number:	Date:
Customer:	P.O. Number:

Job Description:

The above job has been completed in an acceptable manner and may be billed as 100% complete.

Company Representative	Customer Representative

SECTION IV

WARRANTY INSPECTION

Reminder: Perform warranty inspection approximately one or two months prior to expiration. This will allow time to notify all parties involved.

WARRANTY INSPECTION

WARRANTY INSPECTION DATE		WARRANTY EXPIRATION DATE		
Company Notified of Warranty Inspection			☐ Yes	☐ No
Company Officer Notified (Full Name)				
Company Notified by (Check One)		☐ Letter	☐ Phone	☐ In Person
JOB TITLE				
SPECIFIC LOCATION				
PERSON(S) PRESENT FOR INSPECTION				
Defects Found	☐ Yes	☐ No	Contractor Notified	☐ Yes	☐ No
Describe Defects (Number and Type) and Comment				

Defects Corrected	☐ Yes	☐ No	REPORT #	
			CHECK ONE	☐ PASS ☐ FAIL

WARRANTY INSPECTION

WARRANTY INSPECTION DATE		WARRANTY EXPIRATION DATE		

Company Notified of Warranty Inspection	☐ Yes	☐ No

Company Officer Notified (Full Name)	

Company Notified by (Check One)	☐ Letter	☐ Phone	☐ In Person

JOB TITLE

SPECIFIC LOCATION

PERSON(S) PRESENT FOR INSPECTION

Defects Found	☐ Yes	☐ No	Contractor Notified	☐ Yes	☐ No

Describe Defects (Number and Type) and Comment

Defects Corrected	☐ Yes	☐ No	REPORT #	
			CHECK ONE	☐ **PASS** ☐ **FAIL**

WARRANTY INSPECTION

WARRANTY INSPECTION DATE		WARRANTY EXPIRATION DATE		
Company Notified of Warranty Inspection			☐ Yes	☐ No
Company Officer Notified (Full Name)				
Company Notified by (Check One)		☐ Letter	☐ Phone	☐ In Person
JOB TITLE				
SPECIFIC LOCATION				
PERSON(S) PRESENT FOR INSPECTION				

Defects Found	☐ Yes	☐ No	Contractor Notified	☐ Yes	☐ No
Describe Defects (Number and Type) and Comment					

Defects Corrected	☐ Yes	☐ No	REPORT #	
			CHECK ONE	☐ **PASS** ☐ **FAIL**

WARRANTY INSPECTION

WARRANTY INSPECTION DATE		WARRANTY EXPIRATION DATE		
Company Notified of Warranty Inspection			☐ Yes	☐ No
Company Officer Notified (Full Name)				
Company Notified by (Check One)		☐ Letter	☐ Phone	☐ In Person

JOB TITLE

SPECIFIC LOCATION

PERSON(S) PRESENT FOR INSPECTION

Defects Found	☐ Yes	☐ No	Contractor Notified	☐ Yes	☐ No

Describe Defects (Number and Type) and Comment

Defects Corrected	☐ Yes	☐ No	REPORT #	
			CHECK ONE	☐ **PASS** ☐ **FAIL**

WARRANTY INSPECTION

WARRANTY INSPECTION DATE		WARRANTY EXPIRATION DATE	
Company Notified of Warranty Inspection		☐ Yes	☐ No
Company Officer Notified (Full Name)			
Company Notified by (Check One)	☐ Letter	☐ Phone	☐ In Person

JOB TITLE

SPECIFIC LOCATION

PERSON(S) PRESENT FOR INSPECTION

Defects Found	☐ Yes	☐ No	Contractor Notified	☐ Yes	☐ No

Describe Defects (Number and Type) and Comment

Defects Corrected	☐ Yes	☐ No	REPORT #	
			CHECK ONE	☐ **PASS** ☐ **FAIL**

SECTION V
REFERENCE DATA

COMMON COATING DEFECTS AND ERRORS BY APPLICATION

It is the author's intent to emphasize a few of many known coating failures and encourage further research by the user of this logbook. The reader may already be familiar with these and others such as runs, sags, blisters, peeling, and, of course, rust. The author recommends the following reference sources:

Corrosion Prevention by Protective Coatings (**Third Edition**)—Authored by Charles G. Munger & Revised by Dr. Louis D. Vincent.

Fitz's Atlas of Coating Defects—Compiled by Brendan Fitzsimons, Fitz-Coatings Limited.

Both books are available from NACE Press.

COMMON COATING DEFECTS AND ERRORS BY APPLICATION

Checking **Cracking, Alligatoring**	All caused by stress in the coating film. Checking is very small cracks which do not penetrate the substrate, while cracking and alligatoring will. Both cracking and alligatoring can be caused by a formulation problem. Often cracking and alligatoring, which are much larger than checking, are attributed to expansion, aging, compatibility with the previous coating, or weathering.
Spatter Coat **Holidays**	Each caused by application error. Spatter coat is commonly found at the end of a spray path when the applicator fans out and away from the surface or around bolted patterns. Reflective coatings may camouflage the problem areas and appear to be ok until they begin to rust. Holidays, while similar, are areas of the substrate or previously coated surface that the applicator missed.
Pinpoint Rusting **Pinholes**	Pinpoint rusting and pinholes are similar in that they generally appear in random groups and are often concentrated. While pinpoint rusting may be visible, often pinholes are difficult to see with the naked eye. Pinholes are often discovered with the use of a holiday detector.
Efflorescence	Powdery substance mostly found on concrete, plaster, and similar substrates that causes adhesion failure from migration of salts surfacing through moisture and lifting the coating.
Dry Spray	Uneven sand paper finish often caused by excessive distance from the surface, improper spray gun setting, or use of a fast drying product.

SSPC/NACE JOINT WRITTEN STANDARDS

SSPC DESIGNATION	NACE DESIGNATION	TITLE	WHAT MUST BE REMOVED?	WHAT CAN REMAIN?
SSPC-SP1	NONE	Solvent Cleaning	Grease and oil contamination	No visible grease or oil
SSPC-SP2	NONE	Hand Tool Cleaning	Loosely adhering materials	Tightly adhering materials (2)
SSPC-SP3	NONE	Power Tool Cleaning	Loosely adhering materials	Tightly adhering materials (2)
SSPC-SP5	NACE 1	White Metal Blast	All mill scale, rust and paint	Nothing
SSPC-SP6	NACE 3	Commercial Blast	All mill scale, rust and paint	Up to 33% stains (3)
SSPC-SP7	NACE 4	Brush-off Blast	Loosely adhering materials	Tightly adhering materials (2)
SSPC-SP8	NONE	Pickling	Grease, oil dirt, mill scale and rust	Nothing
SSPC-SP10	NACE 2	Near-white Blast Cleaning	All mill scale, rust and paint	Up to 5% stains (3)
SSPC-SP11	NONE	Power Tool Cleaning to Bare Metal	All mill scale, rust and paint	Nothing (4) Must have minimum 1 mil profile
SSPC-SP13	NACE 6	Preparation of Concrete	N/A	N/A
SSPC-SP14	NACE 8	Industrial Blast	Loosely adhering materials	Up to 10% intact rust, paint or mill scale. Stains on remaining surface permitted (2, 3)
SSPC-SP15	NONE	Commercial Grade Power Tool Cleaning	All mill scale, rust and paint	Up to 33% stains (3, 4). Must have minimum 1 mil profile
SSPC-SP16	NONE	Bush-off Blast Cleaning of Coated and Uncoated Galvanized Steel, Stainless Steels and Non-Ferrous Metals	Visible oil, grease, dirt, dust, metal oxides (corrosion products), and other foreign matter	Intact, tightly adherent coating (2), Must have minimum 0.75 mil profile
SSPC-SP WJ1	NACE WJ1	Waterjet Cleaning of Metals—Clean to Bare Substrates	All visible oil, dirt, corrosion, mill scale, coatings, foreign matter	Discoloration on corroded/pitted steel
SSPC-SP WJ2	NACE WJ2	Waterjet Cleaning of Metals—Very Thorough Cleaning	All visible oil, dirt, corrosion, mill scale, coatings, foreign matter except →	Up to 5% stains or tightly adhering matter (e.g., rust, thin coatings) (2, 3)
SSPC-SP WJ3	NACE WJ3	Waterjet Cleaning of Metals—Thorough Cleaning	All visible oil, dirt, corrosion, mill scale, coatings, foreign matter except →	Up to 5% stains or tightly adhering matter (e.g., rust, thin coatings) (2, 3)
SSPC-SP WJ4	NACE WJ4	Waterjet Cleaning of Metals—Light Cleaning	All visible oil, dirt, corrosion, mill scale, coatings, foreign matter	Tightly adhering matter (2)

1 - Prerequisite to all methods of surface preparation if deposits are visibly evident
2 - Remaining materials are considered tightly adhering if they cannot be loosened with a dull putty knife
3 - Unit of surface area is approximately 9 square inches
4 - Slight residues from paint and rust can remain in the bottom pits if the original surface is pitted

ABRASIVE/PROFILE COMPARATIVE CHART[1]

The following chart should be used only for approximating abrasive size required to obtain a specified anchor pattern. This information can be used for centrifugal wheel as well as pressure blasting. Pressure blasting should be done using 90 to 100 psi nozzle pressure. The depth of anchor pattern used in this chart is an average and not the minimum or maximum depth obtainable.

1 Mil Profile	1.5 Mils Profile
30/60 Mesh Silica Sand	15/35 Mesh Silica Sand
G-80 Steel Grit	G-50 Steel Grit
S-110 Steel Shot*	S-170 Steel Shot*
80 Mesh Garnet	36 Mesh Garnet
100 Aluminium Oxide	50 Grit Aluminum Oxide
Clemtex #4	Clemtex #3
2 Mils Profile	**2.5 Mils Profile**
16/35 Mesh Silica Sand	8/35 Mesh Silica Sand
G-40 Steel Grit	G-40 Steel Grit
S-230 Steel Shot*	S-280 Steel Shot*
36 Mesh Garnet	16 Mesh Garnet
16 Grit Aluminium Oxide	24 Grit Aluminum Oxide
Clemtex #3	Clemtex #2
Black Beauty BB-50 or BB-2040	Black Beauty BB-400
3 to 4 Mils Profile	
8/20 Mesh Silica Sand	
G-25 Steel Grit	
S-330 or 390 Steel Shot*	
16 Mesh Garnet	
16 Grit Aluminum Oxide	
Clemtex #2	
Black Beauty BB-40 or BB-25	

*The steel shot alone will not give a good angular anchor pattern and should be used in combination with steel grit for best results.

[1]From *NACE Corrosion Engineer's Reference Book,* R.S. Treseder, editor, NACE, Houston, TX, 1980, p. 212.

FORMULAS[1]

Wet Film Thickness to Dry Film Thickness

No Solvent Added:

DFT = WFT × % solids by volume

Solvent Added:

$$\text{DFT} = \text{WFT} \times \frac{\%\ \text{solids by volume}}{1 + \%\ \text{thinner by volume}}$$

Dry Film Thickness to Wet Film Thickness

$$\text{WFT} = \frac{\text{DFT}}{\%\ \text{solids by volume}}$$

$$\text{WFT} = \frac{\text{DFT} (1 + \%\ \text{thinner by volume})}{\%\ \text{solids by volume}}$$

Spreading Rate

$$\text{\# of Gallons of coating} \times \%\ \text{solids per gallon} \times \frac{1{,}604}{\#\ \text{mils DFT}} = \text{Coverage in ft}^2$$

$$\text{\# of Liters of coating} \times \%\ \text{solids per liter} \times \frac{1{,}000}{\#\ \text{microns DFT}} = \text{Coverage in m}^2$$

[1]From the NACE International Coating Inspector Training and Certification Program.

TEMPERATURE CONVERSION CHART (°F to °C)

°F	°C	°F	°C	°F	°C
0	-17.8	41	5.0	82	27.8
1	-17.2	42	5.6	83	28.3
2	-16.7	43	6.1	84	28.9
3	-16.1	44	6.7	85	29.4
4	-15.6	45	7.2	86	30.0
5	-15.0	46	7.8	87	30.5
6	-14.4	47	8.3	88	31.1
7	-13.9	48	8.9	89	31.7
8	-13.3	49	9.4	90	32.2
9	-12.8	50	10.0	91	32.8
10	-12.2	51	10.6	92	33.3
11	-11.7	52	11.1	93	33.9
12	-11.1	53	11.7	94	34.4
13	-10.6	54	12.2	95	35.0
14	-10.0	55	12.8	96	35.6
15	-9.4	56	13.3	97	36.1
16	-8.9	57	13.9	98	36.7
17	-8.3	58	14.4	99	37.2
18	-7.8	59	15.0	100	37.8
19	-7.2	60	15.6	110	43.3
20	-6.7	61	16.1	120	48.9
21	-6.1	62	16.7	130	54.4
22	-5.6	63	17.2	140	60.0
23	-5.0	64	17.8	150	65.6
24	-4.4	65	18.3	160	71.1
25	-3.9	66	18.9	170	76.7
26	-3.3	67	19.4	180	82.2
27	-2.8	68	20.0	190	87.8
28	-2.2	69	20.6	200	93.3
29	-1.7	70	21.1	210	98.9
30	-1.1	71	21.7	220	104.4
31	-0.6	72	22.2	230	110.0
32	0	73	22.8	240	115.6
33	0.6	74	23.3	250	121.1
34	1.1	75	23.9	300	148.8
35	1.7	76	24.4	350	176.6
36	2.2	77	25.0	400	204.4
37	2.8	78	25.6	450	232.2
38	3.3	79	26.1	500	260.0
39	3.9	80	26.7	750	398.8
40	4.4	81	27.2	1000	537.7

MILLIMETERS TO INCHES (Decimal & Fractional)

Millimeter	Decimal (Inches)	Nearest Fraction
1	.03937	3/64
2	.07874	5/64
3	.11811	1/8
4	.15748	5/32
5	.19685	13/64
6	.23622	15/64
7	.27559	9/32
8	.31496	5/16
9	.35433	23/64
10	.39370	25/64
11	.43307	7/16
12	.47244	15/32
13	.51181	1/2
14	.55118	35/64
15	.59055	19/32
16	.62992	5/8
17	.66929	43/64
18	.70886	45/64
19	.74803	3/4
20	.78740	25/32
21	.82677	53/64
22	.86614	55/64
23	.90051	29/32
24	.94488	15/16
25	.98425	63/64
26	1.02362	1 1/64
27	1.06299	1 1/16
28	1.10236	1 7/64
29	1.14173	1 9/64
30	1.18110	1 3/16
31	1.22047	1 7/32
32	1.25984	1 17/64
33	1.29921	1 19/64
34	1.33858	1 11/32
35	1.37795	1 3/8
36	1.41732	1 27/64
37	1.45669	1 29/64
38	1.49606	1 1/2
39	1.53543	1 17/32
40	1.57480	1 37/64
41	1.61417	1 39/64
42	1.65354	1 21/32
43	1.69291	1 11/16
44	1.73228	1 47/64
45	1.77165	1 49/64
46	1.81102	1 13/16
47	1.85039	1 27/32
48	1.88976	1 57/64
49	1.92913	1 59/64
50	1.96850	1 31/32
51	2.00787	2 1/64
52	2.04724	2 3/64
53	2.08661	2 5/64
54	2.12598	2 1/8
55	2.16535	2 5/32
56	2.20472	2 13/64
57	2.24409	2 1/4
58	2.28346	2 9/32
59	2.32283	2 21/64
60	2.36220	2 23/64
61	2.40157	2 13/32
62	2.44094	2 7/16
63	2.48031	2 31/64
64	2.51968	2 33/64
65	2.55905	2 9/16
66	2.59842	2 19/32
67	2.63779	2 41/64
68	2.67716	2 43/64
69	2.71653	2 23/32
70	2.75590	2 3/4
71	2.79527	2 51/64
72	2.83464	2 53/64
73	2.87401	2 7/8
74	2.91338	2 29/32
75	2.95275	2 61/64
76	2.99212	2 63/64
77	3.03149	3 1/32
78	3.07086	3 5/64
79	3.11023	3 7/64
80	3.14960	3 5/32
81	3.18897	3 3/16
82	3.22834	3 15/64
83	3.26771	3 17/64
84	3.30708	3 5/16
85	3.34645	3 11/32
86	3.38582	3 25/64
87	3.42519	3 27/64
88	3.46456	3 15/32
89	3.50393	3 1/2
90	3.54330	3 35/64
91	3.58267	3 37/64
92	3.62204	3 5/8
93	3.66141	3 21/32
94	3.70078	3 45/64
95	3.74015	3 47/64
96	3.77952	3 25/32
97	3.81889	3 13/16
98	3.85826	3 55/64
99	3.89763	3 57/64
100	3.93700	3 15/16

MILLIMETERS TO INCHES (Decimal & Fractional)

AREA

Sq. Inches	Sq. Feet	Sq. Yards	Acres	Sq. Miles	Sq. Centimeters	Sq. Meters	Hectares
1	0.00694444	0.000771605	—	—	6.451625806	0.0006451625258	—
144	1	0.1111111	0.00000229568	—	929.0341161	0.09290341	0.0000092903
1296	9	1	0.0002066116	0.0000003228	8361.307045	0.83613071	0.000083613
6272640	43560	4840	1	0.0015625	4046726.10	4046.872610	0.40468726
4014489600	27878400	3097600	640	1	—	2589998.470	258.999847
0.1549997	0.00107639	0.000119599	—	—	1	0.0001	—
1549.9969	10.7638673	1.1959853	0.0002471044	0.0000003861	1000	1	0.0001
15499969	107638.673	11959.8526	2.4710439	0.0000386106	—	10000	1

CAPACITY—VOLUME

Cu. Inches	Cu. Feet	Cu. Yards	Liters	Cu. Meters	U.S. Gallons	Imp. Gallons	Bbls (42 U.S.G.)
1	0.0005787037	0.00002143347	0.01638672	0.00001638716	0.004329004	0.003604675	0.0001030715
1728	1	0.037037037	28.316252	0.02831702	7.4805195	6.228878	0.1781076
46656	27	1	764.5388027	0.7645594	201.974026	168.1797073	4.8089054
61.0250256	0.03531541	0.001307978	1	0.001000027	0.2641776	0.2199754	0.006289943
61023.37796	35.3144548	1.3079428	999.9730008	1	264.1704674	219.9694326	6.289773
231	0.1336806	0.004951132	3.7853323	0.003785434	1	0.8326799	0.02380952
277.4175359	0.1605426	0.005946021	4.5459635	0.004546086	1.2009417	1	0.02859385
9702	5.6145833	0.2079475	158.9839563	0.1589882	42	34.9725549	1

U.S. STANDARD MESH SPECIFICATIONS

Mesh	Opening in Inches	Microns	Mesh	Opening in Inches	Microns	Mesh	Opening in Inches	Microns	Mesh	Opening in Inches	Microns
3½	.221	5660	14	.055	1410	40	.0138	350	140	.0041	105
4	.185	4760	16	.046	1190	50	.0116	297	170	.0035	88
5	.156	4000	18	.0390	1000	60	.0097	250	200	.0029	74
6	.131	3360	20	.0328	840	70	.0082	210	230	.0024	62
7	.110	2830	25	.0276	710	80	.0069	177	270	.0021	53
8	.093	2380	30	.0232	590	100	.0058	149	325	.0017	44
10	.078	2000	35	.0195	500	120	.0049	125	400	.0015	37
12	.065	1680									

VARIOUS SIZES OF CYLINDRICAL TANKS

| Capacity in Barrels | Tank Dimensions in Feet and Inches | | Reel Area in Sq. Ft. | Shall Area in Sq. Ft. |
	Diameter	Height		
150	10-0	10-3	80	315
300	12-0	15-0	115	565
500	20-0	10-0	315	630
1,000	20-0	16-0	315	1,130
2,000	25-0	24-0	490	1,885
3,000	25-0	36-0	490	2,890
5,000	30-0	40-0	705	3,770
5,000	35-0	30-0	960	3,300
10,000	42-6	40-0	1,415	5,340
10,000	45-0	36-0	1,590	5,090
15,000	48-0	48-0	1,810	7,240
15,000	52-0	40-0	2,125	6,535
20,000	60-0	40-0	2,825	7,540
25,000	67-0	40-0	3,525	8,420
30,000	67-0	48-0	3,525	10,100
30,000	73-4	40-0	4,230	9,335
35,000	80-0	40-0	5,025	10,055
45,000	90-0	40-0	6,380	11,310
55,000	100-0	40-0	7,855	12,565
80,000	110-0	48-0	9,500	16,590
80,000	120-0	40-0	11,310	15,080
100,000	134-0	40-0	14,100	16,840
125,000	150-0	40-0	17,670	18,850
150,000	150-0	48-0	17,670	22,620
180,000	180-0	40-0	25,470	22,620
268,000	200-0	48-0	31,415	30,160

SPHERES

Diameter in Ft.	Capacity in Barrels	Surface of Sphere in Sq. Ft.
20	746	1,257
25	1,457	1,963
30	2,518	2,827
35	3,998	3,848
40	5,969	5,027
45	8,498	6,362
50	11,657	7,854
55	15,515	9,503
60	20,142	11,310
65	25,608	13,273
70	31,984	15,394

FLAT PLATES

Thickness in Inches	Weight Per Sq. Ft.	Sq. Ft. Per Ton One Side Only
$1/14$	2.55 lbs./ft^2	784
$1/8$	5.10 lbs./ft^2	392
$3/16$	7.65 lbs./ft^2	261
$1/4$	10.20 lbs./ft^2	196
$3/8$	15.30 lbs./ft^2	131
$1/2$	20.40 lbs./ft^2	98
$5/8$	25.50 lbs./ft^2	78
$3/4$	30.60 lbs./ft^2	65
$7/8$	35.70 lbs./ft^2	58
1	40.80 lbs./ft^2	49

If 2 surfaces are desired, multiply the right column by 2.

HOW TO ESTIMATE SQUARE FOOT COVERAGE FOR DIFFERENT SHAPES

TRIANGLE

To find the number of sq. ft. in any shape triangle or 3 sided surface, multiply the height by the width and divide the total by 2.

$$\begin{array}{r} 40' \text{ height} \\ \times 50' \text{ width} \\ \hline 2,000 \text{ ft}^2 \end{array} \qquad \begin{array}{r} 1,000 \text{ ft}^2 \\ 2\overline{)2,000 \text{ ft}^2} \end{array}$$

SQUARE

Multiply the base measurement in feet times the height in feet.

$$40' \times 40' = 1,600 \text{ ft}^2$$

CYLINDER

When circumference (distance around cylinder) is known, multiply height by circumference.

$$\begin{array}{r} 157' \text{ diameter} \\ \times 100' \text{ diameter} \\ \hline 15,700 \text{ ft}^2 \end{array}$$

When diameter (distance across) is known, multiply diameter by 3.1416. This gives circumference. Then multiply by height.

$$\begin{array}{r} 3.1416 \\ \times 50 \text{ diameter} \\ \hline 157.0800 \text{ ft} \end{array} \qquad \begin{array}{r} 157' \\ \times 100' \text{ diameter} \\ \hline 15,700 \text{ ft}^2 \end{array}$$

Note: Figures do not include end area. See circle.

SPHERE

To find the number of sq. ft. of a sphere or ball, multiply the diameter (distance across) by itself and then multiply this total by 3.1416. If you haven't the diameter, you can find it by measuring the circumference and multiplying it by .31831.

$$\begin{array}{r} 50' \text{ diameter} \\ \times 50' \text{ diameter} \\ \hline 2,500 \text{ ft}^2 \end{array} \qquad \begin{array}{r} 2,500 \\ \times 3.1416 \\ \hline 7,854.0000 \text{ ft}^2 \end{array}$$

RECTANGLE

Multiply the base measurement in feet times the height in feet.

$$20' \times 40' = 800 \text{ ft}^2$$

CIRCLE

To find the number of sq. ft. in a circle, multiply the diameter (distance across) by itself and then multiply this total by .7854.

$$\begin{array}{r} 50' \text{ diameter} \\ \times 50' \text{ diameter} \\ \hline 2,500 \text{ ft}^2 \end{array} \qquad \begin{array}{r} 2,500 \\ \times .7854 \\ \hline 1,969 \text{ ft}^2 \end{array}$$

AREAS OF PIPE PRODUCT

Size—Inside Diameter	Square Feet Per Linear Feet—Exterior	Size—Inside Diameter	Square Feet Per Linear Feet—Exterior
1/2"	0.13'	14"	3.67'
1"	0.34'	16"	4.20'
2"	0.62'	18"	4.92'
3"	0.92'	20"	5.24'
4"	1.18'	24"	6.48'
5"	1.46'	30"	7.85'
6"	1.73'	36"	9.42'
8"	2.26'	40"	10.47'
10"	2.81'	48"	12.56'
12"	3.35'	60"	15.71'

CORRUGATED METALS	SIDING

CORRUGATED METALS

2½" Corrugated Sheet—
To find width before corrugation
multiply the width after
corrugation by 1.08. Assume
depth to be ⅝".

1¼" Corrugated Sheet—
To find width before corrugation
multiply the width after
corrugation by 1.11.
Assume depth to be ³/₈".

SIDING

If the siding has a cross-section view similar to that shown multiply each square foot of area by 1.5 for actual surface area. Double for both sides.

If the siding has a cross-section view similar to that shown multiply each square foot of area by 1.42 for actual surface area. Double for both sides.

If the siding has a cross-section view similar to that shown multiply each square foot of area by 1.75 for actual surface area. Double for both sides.

If the depth is 3", multiply by 1.5. Double for both sides.

ROOF DECK

If the roof deck has a cross-section view similar to that shown, first figure the square foot area then multiply by 2.42 to obtain the actual surface area.

If the roof deck has a cross-section view similar to that shown, figure the top side as just the square foot area of surface. Figure the under-side as follows:
A. For each square foot area
B. multiply by 1.63 for actual surface area.
C. Multiply by 1.75.
D. Multiply by 1.92.

STACKS

To compute the square foot area of a stack, multiply height (B) by the average diameter (A) and multiply that total by 3.

EXAMPLE: Diameter of stack at the top = 5 ft.
Diameter of stack at the bottom = 15 ft.
Average diameter = 10 ft ([5 + 15]÷2).
Height=60 ft. 60×10 = 600.
600×3 = 1,800 ft² of surface area.

VARIOUS SIZES OF ELEVATED WATER TANKS*

CAPACITY (Thousand Gallons)	RISER (Diameter)	INSIDE AREA (FT²)	OUTSIDE AREA + (FT²)
50	4'	3,150	6,500
100	4'	4,300	8,000
150	4'	5,100	9,900
200	4'	5,900	11,100
250	4'	6,700	12,700
500	5'	10,000	19,600
750	Dry 8'	13,600	29,100
1,000	Dry 8'	17,000	36,900

*Low Water Level 100 ft above grade.
+Includes supporting columns

301

COST PER MIL/FT² DETERMINATION

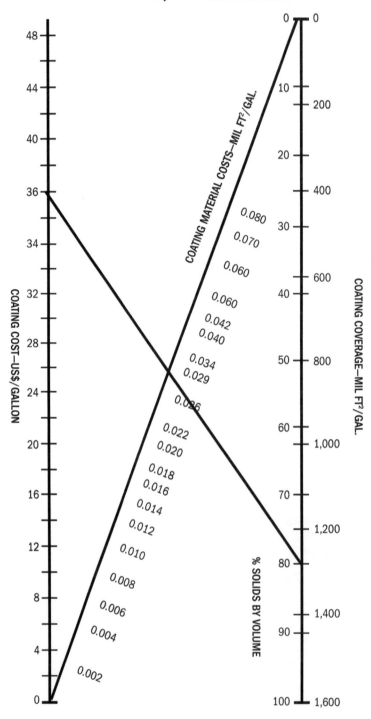

CONVERSION TABLES[1]

TABLE 1: LIQUID MEASUREMENT

01 Gallon (Gal)	Quart (qt)	Pint (pt)	Ounce (oz)	Liter (L)	Milliliter (ml)	Cubic Centimeter (cc)	Cubic Inch
1.0	4.0	8.0	128	3.785	3785	3785	231.0
.250	1.0	2.0	32	0.946	946	946	57.75
.125	0.50	1.0	16	.0473	473	173	28.875
.0078	.031	.063	1.0	.0296	29.6	29.6	1.8
.264	1.057	2.114	33.81	1.0	1000	1000	61
.00026	.001	.002	.034	.001	1.0	1.0	.061
.0043	0.173	.35	.55	0.16	16.39	16.39	1.0

TABLE 2: LENGTH

Yard (yd)	Foot (ft)	Inch (in)	Mil	Micron	Millimeter (mm)	Centimeter (cm)	Meter
1	3	36	36,000	914,400	914.4	91.44	.9144
.333	1	12	12,000	304,800	304.8	30.48	.3048
.028	.083	1	1000	25,400	25.4	2.54	.025
.00028	.00083	.001	1	25.4	.0254	.00254	.0000254
.0000011	.0000033	.000039	.0393	1	.001	.0001	.000001
.00109	.00328	.03937	39.37	1000	1	.1	.001
.0109	.0328	.3937	393.7	10,000	10	1	.01
1.0936	3.280	39.37	39,370	1,000,000	1000	100	1

(1) From NACE International Coating Inspector Training and Certification Program.

CONVERSION TABLES[1] (CONTINUED)

TABLE 3: AREA

Square Yard (yd²)	Square Foot (ft²)	Square Inch (in²)	Square Millimeter (mm²)	Square Centimeter (cm²)	Square Meter (m²)
1	9	1296	836,127.36	8,361.27	.83612
.1111	1	144	92,903.04	929.03	.0929
.00007716	.006944	1	645.16	6.4516	.0006452
.0000012	.0000108	.001551	1	.01	.000001
.0001196	.001076	.155	100	1	.0001
1.196	10.76	155.00	1,000,000	10,000	1

TABLE 4: PRESSURE

Pounds per ft²	Pounds per in²	Kilograms per cm²	Kilograms Pascal
1	.00694	.000488	.0479
144	1	.0703	6.895
2048	14.22	1	98.07
.0208	.000145	.0000102	1

TABLE 5: WEIGHT

Pounds (lb)	Ounce (oz)	Gram (gm)	Kilogram (kg)
1	16	453.6	.4536
.0625	1	28.34	.02834
.02206	.0353	1	.001
2.206	35.3	1000	1

(1) From NACE International Coating Inspector Training and Certification Program.

RELATIVE HUMIDITY, PERCENT = FAHRENHEIT TEMPERATURES
(Pressure = 30.0 in)

AIR TEMP.	DEPRESSION OF WET-BULB THERMOMETER															
	0.5	1.0	1.5	2.0	2.5	3.0	3.5	4.0	4.5	5.0	5.5	6.0	6.5	7.0	7.5	8.0
35	95	91	86	81	77	72	67	63	58	54	49	45	40	36	32	27
37	95	91	87	83	78	74	69	65	61	57	53	48	44	40	36	31
39	96	92	87	83	79	75	71	67	63	59	55	51	47	43	39	35
40	96	92	87	83	79	75	71	68	64	60	56	52	48	45	41	37
42	96	92	88	85	81	77	73	69	65	62	58	55	51	47	44	40
44	96	93	89	85	81	78	74	71	67	63	60	56	53	49	46	43
45	96	93	89	86	82	78	74	71	67	64	61	57	54	51	47	44
47	96	93	89	86	82	79	75	72	69	66	62	59	56	53	49	46
49	96	93	90	86	83	80	76	73	70	67	64	61	57	54	51	48
50	96	93	90	87	83	80	77	74	71	67	64	61	58	55	52	49
52	97	94	90	87	84	81	78	75	72	69	66	63	60	57	54	51
54	97	94	91	88	85	82	79	76	73	70	67	64	61	59	56	53
55	97	94	91	88	95	82	79	76	73	70	68	65	62	59	57	54
57	97	94	91	88	85	82	80	77	74	71	69	66	63	61	58	55
59	97	94	91	89	86	83	80	78	75	72	70	67	65	62	59	57
60	97	94	91	89	86	83	81	78	75	73	70	68	65	63	60	58
62	97	94	92	89	86	84	81	79	76	74	71	69	66	64	61	59
64	97	95	92	90	87	84	82	79	77	74	72	70	67	65	63	60
65	97	95	92	90	87	85	82	80	77	75	72	70	68	66	63	61
67	97	95	92	90	87	85	83	80	78	75	73	71	69	65	64	62
69	97	95	93	90	88	85	83	81	79	76	74	72	70	67	65	63
71	98	95	93	90	88	86	84	81	79	77	75	72	70	68	66	64
73	98	95	93	91	88	86	84	82	80	78	75	73	71	69	67	65
75	98	96	93	91	89	86	84	82	80	78	76	74	72	70	68	66
77	98	96	93	91	89	87	85	83	81	79	77	74	72	71	69	67
79	98	96	93	91	89	87	85	83	81	79	77	75	73	71	69	68

RELATIVE HUMIDITY, PERCENT = FAHRENHEIT TEMPERATURES
(Pressure = 30.0 in)

AIR TEMP	DEPRESSION OF WET-BULB THERMOMETER										
	1	2	3	4	5	6	7	8	9	10	11
80	96	91	87	83	79	75	72	68	64	61	57
84	96	92	88	84	80	76	73	69	66	62	59
88	96	92	88	85	81	77	74	70	67	64	61
90	96	92	89	85	81	78	74	71	68	65	61
94	96	93	89	85	82	79	75	72	69	66	63
98	96	93	89	86	83	79	76	73	70	67	64
100	96	93	89	86	83	80	77	73	70	68	65
104	97	93	90	87	83	80	77	74	71	69	66
108	97	93	90	87	84	81	78	75	72	70	67
110	97	93	90	87	84	81	78	75	73	70	67

TEMPERATURE OF DEW POINT IN DEGREES FAHRENHEIT
(Pressure = 30.0 in)
Depression of Wet-Bulb Thermometer (t-t')

Air Temperature (t)	Vapor Pressure (e)	2.0	4.0	6.0	8.0	10.0	12.0	14.0	16.0	18.0	20.0
30	0.164	25	18	8	-7						
32	.180	27	21	12	-1	-42					
34	.195	29	23	16	+5	-17					
36	.211	31	26	19	10	-6					
38	.228	33	28	22	14	+1	-36				
40	0.247	35	30	25	18	7	-14				
42	.266	38	33	27	21	12	-3				
44	.287	40	35	30	24	16	+4	-24			
46	.310	42	37	32	27	20	10	-7			
48	.334	44	40	35	29	23	14	+1	-41		
50	0.360	46	42	37	32	26	18	8	-13		
52	.387	48	44	40	34	29	22	13	-2		
54	.417	50	46	42	37	32	25	18	+6	-20	
56	.448	53	49	44	40	34	29	22	12	-5	
58	.482	55	51	47	42	37	32	25	17	+4	-30
60	0.517	57	53	49	45	40	35	29	21	11	-8
62	.555	59	55	52	47	43	38	32	25	16	-3
64	.595	61	57	54	50	46	41	35	29	21	+11
66	.638	63	60	56	52	48	44	38	32	26	17
68	.684	65	62	58	55	51	46	42	36	29	22

TEMPERATURE OF DEW POINT IN DEGREES FAHRENHEIT

(Pressure = 30.0 in)

Depression of Wet-Bulb Thermometer (t-t')

Air Temperature (t)	Vapor Pressure (e)	2.0	4.0	6.0	8.0	10.0	12.0	14.0	16.0	18.0	20.0
70	.0732	67	64	61	57	53	49	44	39	33	26
72	.783	69	66	63	59	56	52	47	42	37	30
74	.838	71	68	65	62	58	54	50	45	40	34
76	.896	73	70	67	64	60	57	53	48	43	38
78	.957	75	72	69	66	63	59	55	51	46	41
80	1.022	77	74	72	68	65	62	58	54	50	44
82	.091	79	77	74	71	67	64	60	57	52	48
84	.163	81	79	76	73	70	66	63	59	55	51
86	.241	83	81	78	75	72	69	65	62	58	54
88	1.322	85	83	80	77	74	71	68	64	61	57
90	1.408	87	85	82	79	76	73	70	67	63	59
92	.499	89	87	84	81	79	76	73	69	66	62
94	.595	92	89	86	84	81	78	75	72	68	65
96	.696	94	91	88	86	84	80	77	74	71	67
98	.803	96	93	90	88	86	82	79	76	73	70
100	1.916	98	95	93	90	87	85	82	79	76	72
102	2.035	100	97	95	92	89	87	84	81	78	75
104	.160	102	99	97	94	92	89	86	83	80	77
106	.292	104	101	99	96	94	91	88	86	83	80
108	.431	106	103	101	98	96	93	91	88	85	82
110	2.576	108	105	103	100	98	95	93	90	87	84

RATING OF PAINTED SURFACE
ASTM-D610/SSPC-Vis 2

SCALE AND DESCRIPTION OF RUST GRADES

Rust Grades*	Description	ASTM-SSPC Photographic Standard
10	no rusting or less than 0.01 percent of surface rusted	unnecessary
9	minute rusting less than 0.03 percent of surface rusted	No. 9
8*	few isolated rust spots. less than 0.1 percent of surface rusted	No. 8
7	less than 0.3 percent of surface rusted	none
6*	extensive rust spots but less than 1 percent of surface rusted	No. 6
5	rusting to the extent of 3 percent of surface rusted	none
4*	rusting to the extent of 10 percent of surface rusted	No. 4
3*	approximately one sixth of the surface rusted	none
2	approximately one third of the surface rusted	none
1	approximately one half of the surface rusted	none
0*	approximately 100 percent of the surface rusted	unnecessary

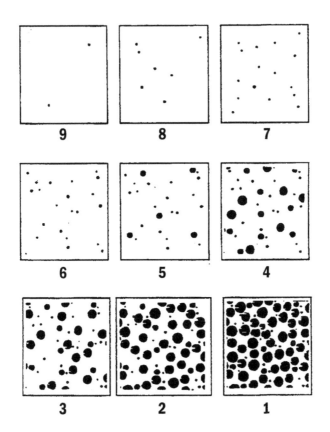

DECODED BATCH NUMBERS

The eight decoded batch numbers on the following page represent examples only. The intent is to illustrate how to verify the shelf life of a particular manufacturer's coating. The inspector/project foreman should know that batch numbers are frequently used to date the coating and indicate the particular plant where the coating was manufactured. *This is only a short list.* The inspector/project foreman is encouraged to contact the manufacturer of the particular coating for further assistance. It is important to verify the most current batch number definition.

GLOSSARY

Plant   The batch plant where the paint was manufactured.

Year   The year the coating was batched. Usually this is symbolized by a single or double numeral digit, such as 04 or 4 meaning 94.

Month   The month the coating was batched. Usually this is symbolized by a single letter, numeral digit, or double numeral digit. The letter A would symbolize Jan., B for Feb., and so on. The digits 3 or 03 would symbolize March.

NOD   The exact day within a 365-day year the coating was batched. Usually this is symbolized by 3 numeral digits, such as 003 or 365. Jan. 3 would be 003. Dec. 31 would be 365.

Week   The exact week within a given year the coating was batched. The numeral digits 38 would symbolize the 38th week of the given year.

DECODED BATCH NUMBERS

Legend: **P**   Plant
           Y   Year
           M   Month
           NOD   Number of Days in the Year
           W   Number of Weeks

Sherwin Williams ...... O D 2 6 0 4 R
           P **NOD** **Y**

International............. R A 6 2 9 2 U H 1   (Year began year with 2000
           Y M   **P**   and they skipped the letter "I")
                                      If manufactered in the year 2015,
                                      the first letter will be R. The
                                      second letter represents month of
                                      manufacture (A = January). The
                                      last two letters = manufacturing
                                      site (UH = Houston)

Carboline .... 3 M 4 9 6 1 L   Mfg omits 1 in the month
           Y M   **P**

Ameron .... 9 3 3 3 4 9 9 9 1 7   9 = manufacturing site
           P Y   **M**   3 = the year 2015
                                        33 = the 33rd week of the year =
                                      August 11-17

Devoe.......................... B 4 7 0 9 3 H U 3 D
                         P Y M

Tnemec .... K C 2 0 0 4 0 9 1 2 3 4
           P   **Y**   **M**

PPG............................. 9 3 3 3 4 9 9 9 1 7   9 = manufacturing site
           P Y   **M**   3 = the year 2015
                                          33 = the 33rd week of the year =
                                      August 11-17

Sigma.......................... 9 3 3 3 4 9 9 9 1 7   9 = manufacturing site
           P Y   **M**   3 = the year 2015
                                          33 = the 33rd week of the year =
                                      August 11-17

Hempel 4 2 5 0 4 1 2 3 4
           P Y **M**

Note: several companies refuse to reveal this information.
Batch number identification is subject to change without notice. If in
doubt, contact your vendor.

PROFILE TAPE, TRANSPARENT TAPE, AND NOTES

PROFILE TAPE, TRANSPARENT TAPE, AND NOTES

Pages 316–330 are reserved for daily field tests including, but not limited to, profile tape & transparent tape for lifting visible oil, loose paint, and other contaminants from a substrate.

See Example Below:

Hand-write description
of tape under each test

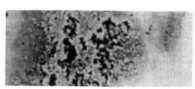

Visible Oil
Date:
Structure:
Specific location:

Loose Paint
Date:
Structure:
Specific location:

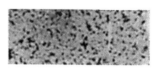

Loose Rust
Date:
Structure:
Specific location:

Job Title: _____

Standard Specified: _____

Achieved: ☐ Yes   ☐ No_____

Report #:_____

PROFILE TAPE, TRANSPARENT TAPE, AND NOTES

Job Title: _____

Standard Specified: _____

Achieved: ☐ Yes   ☐ No_____

Report #:_____

PROFILE TAPE, TRANSPARENT TAPE, AND NOTES

Job Title: _____

Standard Specified: _____

Achieved: ☐ Yes   ☐ No_____

Report #:_____

PROFILE TAPE, TRANSPARENT TAPE, AND NOTES

Job Title: _____

Standard Specified: _____

Achieved: ☐ Yes   ☐ No_____

Report #:_____

PROFILE TAPE, TRANSPARENT TAPE, AND NOTES

Job Title: _____

Standard Specified: _____

Achieved: ☐ Yes   ☐ No_____

Report #:_____

PROFILE TAPE, TRANSPARENT TAPE, AND NOTES

Job Title: _____

Standard Specified: _____

Achieved: ☐ Yes   ☐ No_____

Report #:_____

PROFILE TAPE, TRANSPARENT TAPE, AND NOTES

Job Title: _____

Standard Specified: _____

Achieved: ☐ Yes   ☐ No_____

Report #:_____

PROFILE TAPE, TRANSPARENT TAPE, AND NOTES

Job Title: _____

Standard Specified: _____

Achieved: ☐ Yes   ☐ No_____

Report #:_____

PROFILE TAPE, TRANSPARENT TAPE, AND NOTES

Job Title: _____

Standard Specified: _____

Achieved: ☐ Yes   ☐ No_____

Report #:_____

PROFILE TAPE, TRANSPARENT TAPE, AND NOTES

Job Title: _____

Standard Specified: _____

Achieved: ☐ Yes   ☐ No_____

Report #:_____

PROFILE TAPE, TRANSPARENT TAPE, AND NOTES

Job Title: _____

Standard Specified: _____

Achieved: ☐ Yes ☐ No _____

Report #: _____

PROFILE TAPE, TRANSPARENT TAPE, AND NOTES

Job Title: _____

Standard Specified: _____

Achieved: ☐ Yes ☐ No_____

Report #:_____

PROFILE TAPE, TRANSPARENT TAPE, AND NOTES

Job Title: _____

Standard Specified: _____

Achieved: ☐ Yes   ☐ No_____

Report #:_____

PROFILE TAPE, TRANSPARENT TAPE, AND NOTES

Job Title: _____

Standard Specified: _____

Achieved: ☐ Yes   ☐ No_____

Report #:_____

PROFILE TAPE, TRANSPARENT TAPE, AND NOTES

Job Title: _____

Standard Specified: _____

Achieved: ☐ Yes   ☐ No_____

Report #:_____

PROFILE TAPE, TRANSPARENT TAPE, AND NOTES

Job Title: _____

Standard Specified: _____

Achieved: ☐ Yes ☐ No_____

Report #: _____

SECTION VI
WORK VERIFICATION DATA

WORK EXPERIENCE SUMMARY

NACE and SSPC require both field experience and units of study credit to retain various certification titles. This section lends a space to document and retain such information and keep it readily available for the re-certification process.

SUMMARY OF PROTECTIVE COATINGS
RELATED WORK EXPERIENCE

The coating inspector or coatings person from time to time must recertify. Thus a record of experience must be maintained to track the necessary points needed. It is recommended that this sheet be filled out, copied, and filed. This information may also prove useful as a reference to maintain one's resume.

SUMMARY OF PROTECTIVE COATINGS-RELATED WORK EXPERIENCE
NACE/SSPC Certification Process

APPLICANT INFORMATION	
Name:	Phone:
Company:	Fax:
Address:	E-mail:
City:	State/Province:
ZIP/Postal Code:	Country:

Please summarize below the information on each Individual Job Documentation. List your experience beginning with the most recent, followed by less recent experience.

From Month/Year	To Month/Year	Number of Months in Job	Job Title	Job Performed at (Company Name)

CORROSION RELATED CLASSROOM CREDIT UNITS

Course Title	Date of Class	Location	# of Units

Have you authored or revised a technical book? ☐ Yes ☐ No		# of points:	
Book Title:		Date Published or Revised:	

Have you authored & presented a technical paper? ☐ Yes ☐ No		# of points:	
Title:	Date:	Published Where:	

SUMMARY OF PROTECTIVE COATINGS-RELATED WORK EXPERIENCE
NACE/SSPC Certification Process

APPLICANT INFORMATION	
Name:	Phone:
Company:	Fax:
Address:	E-mail:
City:	State/Province:
ZIP/Postal Code:	Country:

**Please summarize below the information on each Individual Job Documentation.
List your experience beginning with the most recent, followed by less recent experience.**

From Month/Year	To Month/Year	Number of Months in Job	Job Title	Job Performed at (Company Name)

CORROSION RELATED CLASSROOM CREDIT UNITS			
Course Title	Date of Class	Location	# of Units

Have you authored or revised a technical book? ☐Yes ☐ No	# of points:	
Book Title:	Date Published or Revised:	

Have you authored & presented a technical paper? ☐Yes ☐ No	# of points:	
Title:	Date:	Published Where:

337

SUMMARY OF PROTECTIVE COATINGS-RELATED WORK EXPERIENCE
NACE/SSPC Certification Process

APPLICANT INFORMATION	
Name:	Phone:
Company:	Fax:
Address:	E-mail:
City:	State/Province:
ZIP/Postal Code:	Country:

Please summarize below the information on each Individual Job Documentation. List your experience beginning with the most recent, followed by less recent experience.

From Month/Year	To Month/Year	Number of Months in Job	Job Title	Job Performed at (Company Name)

CORROSION RELATED CLASSROOM CREDIT UNITS

Course Title	Date of Class	Location	# of Units

Have you authored or revised a technical book? ☐Yes ☐ No	# of points:	
Book Title:	Date Published or Revised:	
Have you authored & presented a technical paper? ☐Yes ☐ No	# of points:	
Title:	Date:	Published Where:

INDEX

NOTES